# Building a System of Tens
## Calculating With Whole Numbers and Decimals

Casebook

A collaborative project by the staff and
participants of Teaching to the Big Ideas

Principal Investigators
Deborah Schifter
Virginia Bastable
Susan Jo Russell

Boston, Massachusetts • Chandler, Arizona • Glenview, Illinois • Upper Saddle River, New Jersey

Cuisenaire® is a registered trademark of the Cuisenaire Company of America, Inc.

Multilink™ is a trademark of NES Arnold, Ltd.

Unifix® is a registered trademark of Philograph Publications, Ltd.

ISBN 13: 978-0-13-373313-6
ISBN 10:    0-13-373313-0

1 2 3 4 5 6 7 8 9 10 V031 13 12 11 10 09

# Teaching to the Big Ideas

TEACHER COLLABORATORS   Nancy Buell, Bruce Kamerer, Rose Christiansen, Holli Cook, Sorange DeLoren, Bill Eggl, Marcia Estelle, Rebeka Eston, Trish Farrington, Gail Gilmore, Scott Hendrickson, Jill Bodner Lester, Helen McElroy, Mary McHugh, Amy Morse, Deborah O'Brien, Hilory Paster, Margaret Riddle, Nicole Rigelman, Jan Rook, Sherry Sadjak, Cynthia Schwartz, Karen Schweitzer, Lisa Seyferth, Susan Bush Smith, Vicki Smith, Bert Speelpenning, Elizabeth Sweeney, Carol Walker representing the public schools of Amherst (MA), Bedford County (VA), Belchertown (MA), Bismarck (ND), Boston (MA), Brookline (MA), Cambridge (MA), Hanover County (VA), Jordan (UT), Lincoln (MA), Newton (MA), Northampton (MA), Westfield (MA), Williamsburg (MA) and the Atrium School (MA), Brigham Young University (UT), Foundation for Learning (WA), Mount Holyoke College (MA), and Portland State University (OR)

REVIEWERS AND CONSULTANTS   Thomas Carpenter (University of Wisconsin), Bill Eggl (Bedford County Public Schools, VA), Susan Empson (University of Texas), Benjamin Ford (Sonoma State University, CA), Jill Bodner Lester (Mount Holyoke College, MA), James Lewis (University of Nebraska), Amy Morse (Education Development Center, MA), Katie Rafferty (Houston Independent School District, TX), Nicole Rigelman (Portland State University, OR), Sherry Sajdak (Boston Public Schools), Susan Bush Smith (Springfield Public Schools, MA), Bert Speelpenning (Foundation for Learning, WA), Virginia Stimpson (University of Washington), Joy Whitenack (Virginia Commonwealth University), Paul Webb (Bedford County Public Schools, VA), Beth Williams (Bedford County Public Schools, VA), Lisa Yaffee (independent consultant, VT)

PROJECT EDITOR:   Beverly Cory

DVD DEVELOPMENT   David Smith (David Smith Productions)

**National Science Foundation**

This work was supported by the National Science Foundation under Grant Nos. ESI-9254393 (awarded to EDC), ESI-0095450 (awarded to TERC), and ESI-0242609 (awarded to EDC). Any opinions, findings, conclusions, or recommendations expressed here are those of the authors and do not necessarily reflect the views of the National Science Foundation.

Additional support was provided by the ExxonMobil Foundation.

# C O N T E N T S

Introduction   1

## Chapter 1   Students' addition and subtraction strategies   5

| C A S E | 1 | Do my students think flexibly? Do I?   6 |
| C A S E | 2 | Learning math while teaching   12 |
| C A S E | 3 | Learning to think in terms of tens   13 |
| C A S E | 4 | Keeping it straight   16 |
| C A S E | 5 | Doesn't it take 100 of these to make 10,000   21 |

## Chapter 2   The base ten structure of numbers   29

| C A S E | 6 | Number of days in school   30 |
| C A S E | 7 | One hundred ninety-five   33 |
| C A S E | 8 | Who invented zero anyway?   36 |
| C A S E | 9 | Groups and leftovers   40 |
| C A S E | 10 | Thinking with number lines   43 |
| C A S E | 11 | How many thousands in 437,812?   49 |

## Chapter 3   Making sense of addition and subtraction algorithms   55

| C A S E | 12 | The pink way   56 |
| C A S E | 13 | Subtraction and invented algorithms   62 |
| C A S E | 14 | Partitioning subtraction problems   65 |

## Chapter 4    Multiplication of multidigit numbers    71

CASE    15    $27 \times 4$, or dogs looking for scraps    72

CASE    16    From concept to computation    75

CASE    17    Does it fit?    78

CASE    18    Connecting images of multiplication to algebra    82

## Chapter 5    Division with multidigit numbers    91

CASE    19    Let me count the tens    92

CASE    20    Discussing division    97

CASE    21    Sharing jelly beans    102

CASE    22    Making sense of division    108

## Chapter 6    Place value representation of numbers less than 1    119

CASE    23    Tenths and hundredths    120

CASE    24    Parts of pennies    124

CASE    25    Paragraphs, sentences, words...    131

CASE    26    Why do we need rules?    134

CASE    27    Adding tenths to tenths and hundredths to hundredths    137

## Chapter 7    Multiplying and dividing with decimals    145

CASE    28    Representing decimal products    146

CASE    29    Why do we move the decimal anyway?    152

CASE    30    Quotients as decimals    156

## Chapter 8    Highlights of related research    *by Sophia Cohen*    125

SECTION    1    Written number vs. spoken number    162

SECTION    2    Seeing a ten as "one"    168

SECTION    3    Invented procedures for adding and subtracting    175

SECTION    4    Invented procedures for multiplying and dividing    185

SECTION    5    Understanding decimal fractions    193

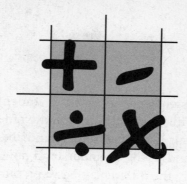

# Introduction

**M**any elementary teachers would rank place value and regrouping as among the most important mathematics topics they teach each year. At the middle school level, the topic of place value is revisited as students work to understand decimals. And many teachers would add that these topics—place value, regrouping, and decimals—are among the most troublesome. Young students frequently lose track of the notion that, say, the 4 in 45 stands for 4 tens. Even at the higher grades, students often have a hard time remembering correct procedures for calculating. Upper-grade teachers frequently report that, although their students have been subtracting multidigit numbers for several years, some persist in subtracting the smaller digit from the larger, even if the larger digit is the one to be subtracted. For example, these students would claim that 342 minus 296 equals 154 instead of 46. And many middle school students ask, "Where do I place the decimal point when I'm adding, and where does it go when I'm multiplying?"

On the surface, it may seem mystifying that so many students, year after year, have such difficulty with these concepts. However, once we delve more deeply into an examination of the ideas underlying the base ten number system, we see that those ideas are quite complex. When students are having difficulty learning the mathematics of the curriculum, the problem is not resolved by dismissing the students as "not made of the right stuff."

1

Indeed, the errors consistently made by many students do have in them elements of logic. For example, when children write ninety-five as 905, they are applying to written numerals what they understand about spoken numbers. By listening to such children and trying to understand how their ideas make sense, we come to see more clearly the differences between our spoken and written systems for representing number; we also identify the ideas that children need to work through.

What are the principles underlying our number system? How do children come to understand these principles? What are the connections that allow students to flexibly maneuver their way around the number system? A second-grade teacher, pondering these questions, wrote:

> Suppose that children can tell you that one place is called the ones place, one the tens place, etc., and that if you have 10 ones, you can't write it in the ones column alone, but you need to write it in the tens column as well, because 10 ones can be traded in for 1 ten and 0 ones. (Jeez, that sounds ridiculously complex!) That knowledge, in my experience, does not ensure that they are able to break numbers apart into tens and ones to make sense of adding double-digit numbers.

This casebook for the Developing Mathematical Ideas (DMI) seminar *Building a System of Tens* is designed to help groups of teachers, as well as others engaged in elementary mathematics education, explore the structure of the base ten number system and the ways students come to understand it. The cases have been written by elementary and middle school teachers, describing episodes from their own classrooms. The teacher-authors, who are themselves working to understand the "big ideas" of the mathematics curriculum, have written these cases as part of their own process of inquiry. They come together on a regular basis to read and discuss one another's work.

The cases are grouped to present students in different classrooms who are working on similar mathematical issues related to the base ten structure of number. Through the cases, we can study children's initial ideas as they talk about how numbers are written and decomposed; the students' application of those ideas as they figure out how to add, subtract, multiply, and divide; and the ways students extend those ideas as they think about decimal fractions.

In chapter 1, the cases look into five classrooms, second through sixth grades, to see how students think about adding and subtracting multidigit numbers. What is it that students must already understand in order to work with numbers in these ways? This question motivates the rest of the casebook. In chapter 2, the cases present students who are working on basic concepts regarding the structure of tens and ones. After some of those concepts have been identified, the cases in chapter 3 once again consider how students bring their understandings of base ten to addition and subtraction. How students apply these basic concepts, and how these concepts can be extended to the work of upper-elementary and middle grades, is the focus of chapters 4 through 7.

Chapter 8, the last in this casebook, is the essay "Highlights of Related Research." This essay summarizes some recent research findings that touch on the issues explored in the cases (chapters 1–7).

When this DMI seminar was first taught, many seminar participants reported that they had to learn how to read the cases.

> It's different from reading a story. I feel as if I've had to comb through each episode with a fine-toothed comb.

> I'm reading cases very slowly, and I'm writing down thoughts about what I'm seeing in the text.

> I find that when I do the same mathematics problems the students in the case are working on, I can better understand what they are doing.

Several teachers offered advice to other participants:

> Read all the cases in a chapter once and try to write down the mathematical issues they raise. You might focus attention on two or three children that interest you and really figure out the mathematical issues that these few children are facing. Try to really understand how the children are thinking. Here's another way to do it: After reading all the cases in a chapter, go over them again, looking for common threads. What mathematical issues connect these cases together?

> Remember that these are glimpses of *real kids* dealing with *real* situations, struggling to make sense of very difficult concepts. Pay particular attention to the *natural* ways students often solve problems.

> Begin with the chapter introduction, which alerts you to the ideas you should pay attention to.

> If possible, discuss the cases informally with other participants before the sessions. If you're unable to do any or some of the above, by all means don't *not* come to the seminar!

As the seminar proceeds, you might talk to other participants about the ways they read the cases to prepare for seminar discussions.

# C H A P T E R
# 1
# Students' addition and subtraction strategies

| CASE 1 | Do my students think flexibly? Do I? | *Ann, Grade 6, October* |
|---|---|---|
| CASE 2 | Learning math while teaching | *Emily, Grade 2, March* |
| CASE 3 | Learning to think in terms of tens | *Semira, Grade 2, December* |
| CASE 4 | Keeping it straight | *Lucy, Grade 3, November* |
| CASE 5 | Doesn't it take 100 of these to make 10,000? | *Olive, Grade 6, September* |

While participating in a professional development program one summer, Ann, a sixth-grade teacher, watched a videotape in which second graders presented their personal methods for solving two-digit addition and subtraction problems. For a problem such as 16 + 28, none of the children used the method most familiar to her: "6 + 8 is 14, so you put down the 4 and carry the 1…." Instead, the children had ways of teasing the numbers apart and recombining them to find the sum or difference. Ann and her colleagues (who were also viewing the video) had to work hard to understand what the children were doing, but they discovered that the children's methods did make sense. When Ann met with her new group of sixth graders the following autumn, she was curious about whether these students, too, might have ways to solve problems that are different from the traditional "carry" and "borrow" procedures—and so she asked them. She describes the resulting classroom discussions in case 1.

Cases 2–5 also describe the work of students who have developed procedures for solving multidigit addition and subtraction problems. Each case illustrates students' insights—sometimes insights that grow out of initial confusion.

Readers are invited to take the time to make sense of what the students are doing. As you read the following cases, try each method with other pairs of numbers and take notes on the following questions: What must students understand in order to devise efficient strategies? What might students learn about the base ten structure of numbers as they work on strategies for addition and subtraction? Will the students' methods work for *any* pair of numbers?

If you teach students younger than these, consider the content at your grade level that will support your students in later years when they encounter the content illustrated in the cases.

If you teach students older than these, consider the content your students encounter that builds on the content illustrated here.

Finally, reread this introduction *after* you read the cases in chapter 1.


CASE 1

# Do my students think flexibly? Do I?

GRADE 6, OCTOBER

My sixth-grade students come to me knowing the U.S. standard algorithms for addition and subtraction. I was wondering how much they really understood about the tens structure of number that these algorithms depend on. I was also curious about how flexible my students

Building a System of Tens

could be in thinking about numbers: How would they manipulate
numbers to solve a problem if they weren't told to use the conventional
algorithms? I didn't believe they could really view addition or subtraction
differently from the way they had been taught for so many years. My
hypothesis was that by the time my students come to sixth grade, the U.S.
standard algorithms have been ingrained in them and will interfere with
their ability to think about math differently.

## Addition strategies

I gave all the students some addition problems orally and asked
them to solve these without any physical aids: no paper, pencils, or
manipulatives. Each problem involved some regrouping. Then I asked
them to explore how they got their answers and to share their individual
thinking with the class. In our class discussions, students shared their
strategies and responded to one another with comments and questions.
To clarify their thinking, they applied each suggested strategy to new
problems. Through this process, I made a number of discoveries.

Students Janae, Tom, and Betsy demonstrated three different
approaches to the same problem, $68 + 24 = ?$

Janae's thinking:

$68 + 24 = ?$

$60 + 20 = 80$

$8 + 4 = 12$

$80 + 12 = 92$

Janae's first step was to add the tens and then the ones, moving
from left to right. This actually seemed to make the regrouping easier,
because of the zero in the 80. Why do we add the way we do, starting
at the right with the ones column? Isn't it easier to add from the left to
the right?

Tom's thinking:

$68 + 24 = ?$

$24 - 2 = 22$

Take the 2 from 24 and add it to the 68 ($68 + 2 = 70$).

Add the 22 which was the answer from $24 - 2$.

$22 + 70 = 92$

Many different questions arose about Tom's thinking, especially the part where he subtracted 2 from 24. Where did the 2 come from? Why did he subtract 2 and not 3 or 4 or any other number? Was the –2 actually the digit 2 in the number 24? Why did he subtract 2 from 24? Why didn't he subtract something from the 68? Eventually, the class concluded that Tom had manipulated the numbers, by taking away and adding on, to create a "nice number" or a number with a zero in the ones. One student stated that "zeros are good."

Betsy's thinking:

$$68$$
$$+\ 24$$

$8 + 4 = 12$

Carry the 1 and add it to the $6 + 2$.

$1 + 6 + 2 = 9$

So the answer is 92.

Betsy's approach is the one I had predicted all my students would use: She pictured 68 and 24 written vertically and applied the traditional algorithm. However, I now feel that this strategy gives a limited view of what is really happening in an addition problem. Does Betsy sense that $6 + 2 + 1 = 9$ really is $60 + 20 + 10 = 90$?

When students answer problems in Betsy's way, we as teachers may presume they know more than they actually do. What do our students really understand when they successfully solve an addition problem the traditional way? Each manipulation of the individual digits seems discrete from every other, rather than part of a connected process. Asking students to give us what we want to hear rather than listening to what they're actually thinking can be very misleading when we are trying to judge what they truly understand.

My hypothesis was partially right and partially wrong. Some students did see addition in the traditional way, but many viewed it in ways that I could not have imagined. Students learned from each other that there are many ways to solve a single problem. Later, one student stated in her journal, "I didn't know there were so many ways to do addition." I didn't, either.

Building a System of Tens

# Ann

GRADE 6, OCTOBER

## Subtraction strategies

The standard subtraction algorithm is a difficult procedure for many | 70
students to understand. Every year at the sixth-grade level, I see some
students still struggling with the regrouping process in subtraction. They
ask themselves, "When do I borrow? Is this where I cross out something?
What if there is a zero in the column I want to take from? When do I
stop borrowing?" They seem to be controlled by the numbers rather than | 75
controlling the numbers themselves. In this process, what the numbers
mean or represent becomes secondary to manipulating the numbers, and
students can quickly get lost.

At the time of this episode, my students had already been investigating
their mental math thinking processes. They had previously investigated | 80
how they did addition "in their heads." By now they were able to explain
orally the addition process they used, and they were starting to record
their steps in written form. The format of the subtraction investigation
was similar to what we had done with addition. I gave all the students
a subtraction problem orally and asked them to solve it without any | 85
physical aids: no paper, pencils, or manipulatives. Again, each problem
involved some regrouping. Then I asked them to explore how they got
their answers and to share their individual thinking with the class. In
follow-up discussions, students responded to one another's strategies
through comments and questions. As with addition, they applied each | 90
strategy to new problems to clarify their thinking. Through this process
they shared the following approaches to the problem 72 − 47 = ?

Jason's thinking:

72 − 47 = ?

First subtract 40 from 72. | 95

72 − 40 = 32

Then subtract 2 (which is part of the 7 of the 47).

32 − 2 = 30

Finally, subtract the remaining 5 from the 30.

30 − 5 = 25 | 100

Interestingly, Jason started on the left with the tens column. Then he
apparently tried to make the number "friendlier," getting a zero in the
ones column by breaking the remaining 7 (of the original 47) into

Chapter 1 9

**2 and 5.** This step seems to eliminate the usual problems associated with borrowing. For Jason, $32 - 2 = 30$ and $30 - 5 = 25$ was easier than $32 - 7 = 25$.

Bert's thinking:

$$72 - 47 = ?$$
$$72 - 10 = 62$$
$$62 - 10 = 52$$
$$52 - 10 = 42$$
$$42 - 10 = 32$$
$$32 - 7 = 25$$

As Jason had done, Bert started on the left with the tens column. He viewed the 47 as $10 + 10 + 10 + 10 + 7$ and subtracted groups of 10. After arriving at the 32, he could solve the remaining part, $32 - 7$.

Holly's idea for $72 - 47$ was similar to Bert's, except that she first took away 2 from both 72 and 47, thus creating a new but equivalent problem: $70 - 45$. She then subtracted in units of 10 four times, and finally subtracted the 5.

Holly's thinking:

$$72 - 47 = ?$$

Take 2 away from both to make $70 - 45$.

$$70 - 10 = 60$$
$$60 - 10 = 50$$
$$50 - 10 = 40$$
$$40 - 10 = 30$$
$$30 - 5 = 25$$

This ability to create a new, equivalent problem by subtracting the same amount from both numbers was thought-provoking for some of my students. Kristy stated, "We could add the same amount to each number and also get the same answer."

Other problems prompted some new ideas from the class. Joe's thinking for $82 - 35$ was first to subtract 2 from 82 and 5 from 35 so he could look at $80 - 30 = 50$. Then he subtracted 5 from 2 and got –3. Finally he subtracted 3 from 50 and got 47.

This strategy fascinated both the class and me. We tried it on many other problems, such as this one:

63 − 25 = ?

63 − 3 = 60 and 25 − 5 = 20

60 − 20 = 40

3 − 5 = −2

40 − 2 = 38

Together we also tried it on a problem that didn't need regrouping:

54 − 22 = ?

54 − 4 = 50 and 22 − 2 = 20

50 − 20 = 30

4 − 2 = 2 ...

At this point, some students realized that we needed to add the 2 to the 30 instead of subtracting it, because there was no regrouping involved:

30 + 2 = 32

For the same problem that Joe talked about, 82 − 35, Jennifer stated that she looked at "subtraction as addition."

82
− 35

First, Jennifer said she would need to "borrow" from the tens column in order to take away 5 from the 2. She explained that she was thinking about it this way: "5 + ? = 12, and 30 + ? = 70. I put in 7 and then 40, for the answer of 47. You can think about it as addition too. Either way, you get the same 47."

After listening to my students and witnessing how very carefully they were paying attention to one another's ideas, I've learned a lot. First, the belief that the U.S. standard algorithm is how elementary students (or even adults like my own summer colleagues) "see" subtraction is far from true. I realize now that students develop their own ideas of what subtraction is and their own notions of how to represent it. This realization has really made me think about how I teach. It's important to understand that when I tell or show students how to do any

## Ann

GRADE 6, OCTOBER

mathematical process, they will interpret the process in many different
ways. Even when all our students can tell us that 57 − 18 = 39, we can't
assume that they all know the exact same things. Giving each of my
students a voice in my math class, and really *listening* to them, is the only
way I will be able to evaluate the depth of their understandings.

170

CASE 2

# Learning math while teaching

## Emily

GRADE 2, MARCH

Recently I watched children solve two-digit subtraction problems. I
was eager to observe their different ways of approaching a problem
and getting an answer that made sense to them. I was prepared to see
confusion and lots of different methods; I felt very open. However, I
was surprised and delighted to learn a new way to solve a two-digit
subtraction problem, one I had never thought of or even imagined before.
I still have to picture it and think it through carefully as I retell it here.

Ivan was working with two or three other kids on the same word
problem that led them each to this equation: 52 − 28 = ? At first, Ivan
said the answer was 36, but Brandon had gotten 24, so now the two were
talking with each other. Brandon saw clearly what Ivan had done and
was explaining to him why it was wrong. Ivan believed him and agreed
with what Brandon said: "20 away from 50 is 30, but you can't take the
2 away from the 8; you have to take the 8 away from the 2 because the 8
is on the bottom."

I imagined Ivan responding "but you can't take the 8 away from the
2 because the 8 is too big." I further imagined encouraging Brandon to
explain more about what he had done, expecting they would talk through
something about borrowing a 10 from the 50 to make the 2 into a 12. But
as I watched, Ivan invented this new method:

"You take the 20 away from the 50 and get 30. Then you take 8 away
from 2, which is −6. Then you take 6 away from 30 and you get 24."

175
180
185
190
195

I've since read Connie Kamii's book (1989) in which she describes several common methods that second graders use to subtract in this situation, and Ivan's method was one of them. It still feels new enough to me that I have to think it through each time. It is definitely a case of my learning some mathematics from my students.

200

CASE 3

# Learning to think in terms of tens

## *Semira*

GRADE 2, DECEMBER

As I work with my students on solving addition and subtraction problems in story contexts, my goal is that students not only develop an understanding of the actions involved in operations, but also take these ideas into higher levels of thinking. Are my students developing efficient numerical strategies? Do they have a deep understanding of operations? I am very concerned about these issues because I know that these early addition and subtraction ideas will later be crucial to their understanding of multiplication, division, and eventually algebra.

205

I recently gave the students an addition problem, first orally, and then on the board. I asked them to close their eyes and describe the action, then tell how they saw it. The problem read as follows:

210

**?** A class of 29 students is going on a trip to the science museum. There are 12 adults going with them. How many people are going on the trip?

215

I checked for understanding of the problem before they went to work on it. I was pleased to find out they all seemed to know that this was an addition situation. I sent them off to work for 10 minutes. While the students worked on the problem, I walked around asking questions about their solving processes. I found that many students could clearly explain their thinking, and I encouraged them to solve the problem in a different way. I noticed that some students finished quickly and others could not

220

finish the task in the given time. Most of those who could not finish were using cubes and counting by ones.

In our class discussion, students shared their strategies. But some students seemed puzzled by the explanations, so I asked many questions to bring more of the class into the ideas.

The following approaches taken by Jorge, David, Angela, and Danny represent all the different strategies used by the class.

Jorge's thinking:

$$29 + 10 = 39 \qquad 12 + 20 = 32$$
$$39 + 1 = 40 \qquad 32 + 8 = 40$$
$$40 + 1 = 41 \qquad 40 + 1 = 41$$

Jorge's first step was to keep one number (29) whole and add the tens from the other number (12), then add ones to get to the next multiple of 10, and then add the rest. Jorge said that it is easier for him to add tens to a number. He also said that he likes to make 10 because it is easier to add numbers this way. His second method of solving the problem (shown at the right) was based on the same approach, but he kept the 12 whole and added the 29 in parts. His explanation to the class seemed very clear to me, but I was concerned about the number of students who seemed puzzled by Jorge's explanation.

David's thinking:

$$\begin{array}{l} \overset{1}{29} \\ 12\ + \\ \hline 41 \end{array} \qquad \begin{array}{l} 29 + 12 = \\ 20 + 12 = 32 \\ 9 + 32 = 41 \end{array} \left| \begin{array}{l} because\ I\ know \\ that\ 9 + 2 = 11 \\ \\ 11 + 30 = 41 \\ \diagup\diagdown \\ \overset{10}{\phantom{.}}\ \overset{1}{+}\ 30 = 40 \\ 40 + 1 = 41 \end{array} \right.$$

I talked to David individually. In response to my request that he explain his first approach (at the left), he said, "I added $9 + 2 = 11$ and I carried over the 1 and added it to the $2 + 1$; then I will add $1 + 2 + 1 = 4$; so my answer is 41." I asked why he had to carry the 1, but he couldn't explain it clearly. He said, "It is sort of like a rule. My father taught me."

When I asked David to explain his second approach, he wrote that he knew that $9 + 2 = 11$.

$$11 + 30 =$$

$$10 + 30 = 40$$

$$40 + 1 = 41$$

250

Then I asked him where we could find the 30 in 29 + 12; he said that he needed to take 1 off 12 and give it to the 29 to make a 30. However, he seemed to be getting more confused about his strategy.

As I look at his work now, it seems that he began his second approach by keeping the 12 whole and adding the 29 in parts. But when he explained to me how he knew 9 + 32 = 41, he lost track of his method and brought in a different idea. Although this idea was valid, too, he lost the connection to his own steps and ended up confused. I now realize it may have been my question that pointed him in a different direction and got him off his own track.

255

260

David has a strong understanding of how to take numbers apart and recombine them. He also knows the steps of the traditional algorithm, but doesn't seem to connect this procedure to what he understands about how numbers are composed of tens and ones. What could be done to help David make those connections?

265

Angela's thinking:

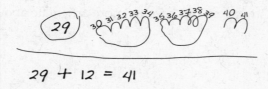

$$29 + 12 = 41$$

The class easily understood Angela's counting-on strategy. She had developed a mental model of the meaning of 29 + 12; this method will always give her the right answer, if done accurately. However, quantities are going to get larger, especially toward the end of second grade. Therefore, Angela will be prone to error as the numbers get larger and more difficult to manage when she counts by 1. I need to think what would be a good next step for Angela, one that will help her to keep her understanding, but also will help her to combine quantities more efficiently.

270

275

Danny's thinking:

I cuoted by 1s.

|||/////|

|||/////| + |||||||| = 41

|||/////|                 ////

*There are 41 students and adults going to the trip.*

Danny's approach really surprised me. I wasn't prepared to see any students doing this. I was even more disappointed to find out that Danny wasn't the only student who counted both quantities by 1. When I asked Danny to explain his thinking, he said, "I draw 29 and 12 sticks." As he explained, he started counting the sticks by 1, but then stopped and said "29," and counted the rest by 1 until stopping at 41. Danny counted on from 29, but he drew the 29 sticks instead of writing the number 29. How can I help Danny and other students who are in the same situation? |280

I know that in first grade, these students did a lot of work on |285 counting by 10, combinations of 10 (e.g., 2 + 8, 6 + 4), and adding 10 (4 + 10, 10 + 16). Now, in second grade, my goal is to have them employ this repertoire to solve problems more efficiently. I will be keeping close watch on Danny and Angela, and on their classmates whose work looks similar, to help them move in this direction. At the |290 same time, I'll be working with students like Jorge and David to help them streamline their strategies and become more articulate about them.

C A S E   4

# Keeping it Straight

## *Lucy*
GRADE 3, NOVEMBER

Over the past few weeks, as I give my third graders two-digit numbers to add, I have been trying to understand what they think is happening with the numbers. In each lesson, students first work in pairs, then share their solutions with the whole class.

At the end of a discussion last week, after the class had already looked at several ways to show that 39 + 52 = 91, Sarah tried to explain yet another way she had found. She understood all the various methods that had been presented. In fact, Sarah is generally very fluent in thinking about how numbers work. This time, when working with her partner, she had tried hard to find an unusual way, hoping she would get to share it during the discussion.

Sarah showed us a stack of 3 cubes and explained that they equaled 30 because she was using one cube to show a ten. She held up a separate stack of 9 and said that, together, the two stacks of cubes represented 39. Then she pointed to a stack of 5 cubes, saying that it was 50 and, with another stack of 2, showed 52. She took the 3-cube and 5-cube stacks and added them together, saying it equaled 80. Then she put the 9-cube and 2-cube "ones" stacks together, saying that they made 11. She then broke off 10 of the 11 cubes, attached them to the 8 cubes representing 80—and looked up confused. She knew that the answer was 91, but her arrangement of cubes didn't look like 91. Class was over, however. It was time for lunch.

I wondered how Sarah was connecting her work on this problem with what she thought she understood about adding. She had demonstrated in earlier lessons that she was already able to use the conventional algorithm to solve this type of problem. When given a similar problem to solve on paper, she had explained that she needed to "carry the 1" because there were too many ones. I wondered what she was thinking when she kept "carrying" the 10 individual cubes.

At the start of math the next day, the class reviewed all the methods they had shared for solving 39 + 52. I asked them to use each method to solve that day's problem, 45 + 39, and then we would discuss what they found.

After the class had been working for a while, I came to Sarah and her partner. They complained that three times they had done it "Sarah's way," and each time the answer was 174. It didn't make sense—they had already reached an answer of 84 doing it other ways. I knew it had really bothered Sarah the day before when the cubes hadn't shown her idea of the right answer. I was pleased with her persistence and joined the pair for a while.

They had built the numbers with Unifix® cubes, using yellow cubes for tens and black for ones. Thus they had 4 yellow and 5 black cubes representing 45, and 3 yellow and 9 black for 39.

335

TEACHER: What happens when you add the two numbers together?

SARAH: First I add the ones together. [*She puts all the black cubes into a stack.*] There are way too many to keep on the ones side, so I try to carry them.

I wanted Sarah to explain what she meant by this.

340

TEACHER: What do you mean, "there are way too many ones to have on the ones side" and you try to carry them? What does that mean?

SARAH: There are 14 ones and I'm doing this like a problem, so I have it, like, I'm sort of writing it, but using cubes instead of writing it.

345

Sarah pointed to the cubes; she had the tens arranged in a column and the ones in another column, vertically, one number below the other.

SARAH: There are too many ones to equal on this side. [*She points to the ones side.*]

TEACHER: OK.

350

SARAH: I carry the 1, so I take 10 away. [*She breaks off 10 of the black cubes.*]

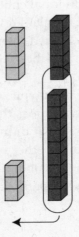

| TEACHER: | What do you mean, you take 10 away? Is that like subtracting? |
|---|---|
| SARAH: | The answer is 14, so I'm trying to carry the 1. [*She is being very patient with all my questions.*] |
| TEACHER: | And what is that 1 that you are trying to carry? |
| SARAH: | The 1 is . . . tens. |
| TEACHER: | OK. |
| SARAH: | Each ten is 10 ones. |
| TEACHER: | OK. |
| SARAH: | So I take away 10 ones. [*She attaches them to the 7 yellow cubes and looks at what she has, a stack of 4 black cubes and a second stack of 17 yellow and black.*] |
| TEACHER: | So you said your answer was 174. |
| SARAH: | And so, here's my tens [*pointing to the yellow and black stack*] and here's my ones. [*Setting aside the 4 black cubes, she begins counting the yellow and black "tens."*] And it's 174. |
| TEACHER: | And this is what you got before. [*Sarah's partner begins counting to make sure.*] |
| SARAH: | [*Pondering*] I'm getting it. [*She has a brightness in her eyes like a light bulb coming on.*] |
| TEACHER: | What do you think? |
| SARAH: | If I put 10 of these up here [*pointing to the 10 black cubes attached above the yellow*] it equals 1, not just 10. |
| TEACHER: | If you put 10 of what up there? [*I want her to be clearer about what she is saying.*] |
| SARAH: | It equals 10 ones. It's 10. Not 100. |
| TEACHER: | I'm not sure I know what you mean. |
| SARAH: | When I took this [10 black cubes] from down here [*pointing back to the 4*], it is a ten. |

355

360

365

370

375

380

Chapter 1

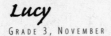

# Lucy

GRADE 3, NOVEMBER

TEACHER: It is a ten?

SARAH: It is *a* ten.

TEACHER: These 10 black Unifix cubes are a ten? [*Sarah picks up an extra yellow cube and attaches it to the other 7 yellow cubes.*] So you're saying this ten [stack of 10 blacks] is the same as this 1 yellow cube?

385

SARAH: [*Nodding and smiling*] It's 84. I know what I was doing wrong now.

TEACHER: You were just thinking of this 10 . . .

SARAH: As being 100.

390

TEACHER: Does your answer of 84 have anything to do with the work you did on your paper when you added the numbers the other ways? What does what you wrote on your paper have to do with what you just found out about that 10?

SARAH: It's the same thing.

395

TEACHER: What was it that you did the same?

SARAH: Like here. [*She picks up the paper on which she applied the traditional algorithm and points to the small 1 she had put above the 4.*] This 1 that I carried is not 10 ones, it's a ten. In the 14, there's a ten right here [*pointing to the digit 1 on her paper*].

400

TEACHER: All right! Are you happy now? [*Sarah smiles.*] That was really bothering you, wasn't it?

Now that I'm writing up this episode, I wish I had thought to ask Sarah what made her realize that the 10 cubes equaled a ten and needed to be represented with a single yellow cube. But I didn't. Maybe next time.

405

It seems to me that Sarah's struggle with representing her work this way helps her make the connection to what's happening on paper when digits are moved around. I'll watch her work in coming days to see if I'm right. Now I have to find that connection for the other 16 kids! What

410

Building a System of Tens

Sarah was trying to show seemed important to me. It was interesting to have that dialogue with her—to go through her thinking with her, watching her ideas become clearer as she talked through her thinking. She was hooked. She knew there was something missing, something wrong, and it was important to her to find it and understand it.

415

C A S E   5

# Doesn't it take 100 of these to make 10,000?

## Olive
GRADE 6, SEPTEMBER

We had just recently spent time reviewing ideas related to the meaning of the four basic operations. I had noticed that students, despite their experience with a reform-based curriculum, were quick to solve most problems using the U.S. standard algorithms. I was curious about what students might do if I asked them to move beyond this approach they use so quickly. When dealing with subtraction of large numbers, might a context encourage them to use landmark numbers such as 500 and 1,000? Would they use models or diagrams when asked to find a second approach? How would they use the concrete materials when the numbers are large? Would they be comfortable with renaming the unit? Where might they struggle? How might I advance their thinking—by having them work with even larger numbers, like 1,000,000? By having them look for patterns in the powers of ten? By having them formulate generalizations related to changing the unit?

420

425

I decided to pose a problem that would involve subtracting 485 from 10,000. I chose the following:

430

**?** Uncle Marvin has $10,000. He needs $485 to buy a remote control wiener dog. He wants to give you the rest of the money. How much will you receive?

# Olive

Knowing that nearly every student could successfully solve this problem with the U.S. standard algorithm (as shown here), I asked them to take a moment to solve the problem in whichever way they chose and share their answers. This way, they would have the answer; then when working on a second approach, they could really spend time thinking about the process, rather than focus on the answer. This move also helped students find errors in their thinking as they worked out their second approach.

$$\begin{array}{r} {}^{0}\cancel{1}{}^{9}\cancel{0}{}^{9}\cancel{0}{}^{9}\cancel{0}{}^{1} \\ 10{,}000 \\ -\ \ \ \ 485 \\ \hline 9{,}515 \end{array}$$

After students shared their answers in their small groups (they had indeed all used the U.S. standard algorithm or a calculator), I presented the following task:

Show at least two different ways to find the solution. Materials available include:

- graph paper
- base ten paper
- 10-by-10 grids
- base ten plastic pieces

As I circulated, I noticed that most students had decided to reassign the value of the 10-by-10 square (hundreds grid) as one thousand. What I had not anticipated was the widespread thinking about what to do from there. Most students next took away 4 hundreds, traded another hundred for 10 tens and took away 8, and then traded a ten for 10 ones and took away 5 (see Figure 1.1). The problem was that they were using the 10-by-10 grid as both 1,000 and 100. Their result was 515, which they recognized was not the same answer they found with the previous method. They had essentially taken 485 from 1,000 rather than 485 from 10,000.

I asked Marc about his thinking and he told me: "I can minus this and this [he crosses off 100s, 10s, and 1s], but I messed up. I was doing 1,000, not 10,000." When I inquired further, he said that he started off using the 10-by-10 grid as 1,000 but when he started taking away, he used it as 100. I commented that he had made an important observation and that I would check in later about what he decided to do to solve this.

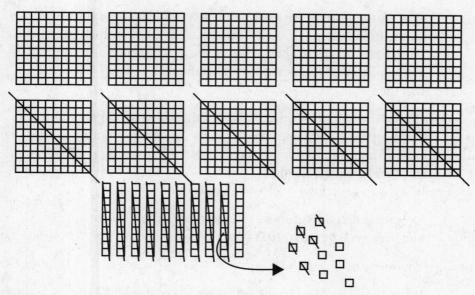

**Figure 1.1** Confusing 1,000 with 100 when modeling 10,000 − 485.

My initial thinking was to partner or group students based on the strategies I saw them using. This way they could have a conversation with someone who was thinking about the problem in similar ways. But discussions began naturally in groups once there was the disequilibrium of one answer with the model and another with the algorithm. I decided to let the conversations that emerged continue rather than try to group students in a different way. I invited students to decide whether they wanted to work with others at their table or continue to work privately.

I was wondering how Keely was thinking about the problem because she seemed puzzled. I thought that asking her to talk aloud about her thinking would help.

TEACHER:   How are you using the base ten pieces to solve this problem?

KEELY:   If this [the 10-by-10 piece] is 1,000, then this [the 1-by-10 piece] is 10, no, 100.

TEACHER:   How did you decide?

470

475

480

Chapter 1

KEELY:     This would be a lot easier if it had 1,000 squares in it. But I have to imagine it. If each little square is 10, then each of these [the 1-by-10 rod] is 10 times 10, or 100. Then the big square is 1,000, because it's 10 hundreds put together.

485

I wondered how she might be thinking about the unit, so I asked, "How are you seeing the $485?" She showed me a collection of four 1-by-10s plus eight small squares, and then suggested that the 5 is half of a 1-by-1 square and sketched a triangle.

490

Then Emily's group called me over with a question.

EMILY:     Doesn't it take 100 of these [*referring to the large square hundreds grid*] to make 10,000?

495

TEACHER:     You tell me.

EMILY:     It has to be, because 10 isn't enough, it's only 1,000. We need stacks of 10 [hundreds] for each thousand, so we'll need 10 of them.

TEACHER:     [*asking the rest of the group*] What do you think about Emily's idea?

500

Ian and Natalie agreed, with Ian commenting, "We have to cut up a lot of stuff to make 10,000." I was confident that with enough time and materials, this group could solve the problem in this way. Another group was using the same approach, but by now had covered the table with a 10-by-10 array of paper hundreds grids to show 10,000 (Figure 1.2). They showed the subtraction by covering up 485, as indicated with the shading, and looking at the difference between the two collections.

505

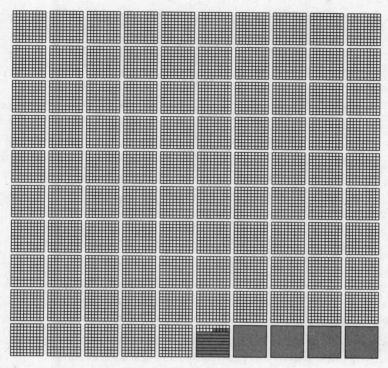

**Figure 1.2** Showing the problem with a 10-by-10 array of hundreds grids.

Isabel started with a square to represent 1,000 and represented 100 and 10 with different-sized rods. She made a sketch to show the problem (Figure 1.3). I asked Isabel to talk to me about why she built the collection this way. She said she knew that she needed to trade pieces in order to take away 485, so she built that into her initial arrangement. She said, "I built it so I had 10,000 but could take away 4 hundreds, 8 tens, and 5 ones." I wondered later if she had done this because of what she learned when solving the problem using the algorithm. Did she see the connection between her approach and borrowing across those zeros?

510

515

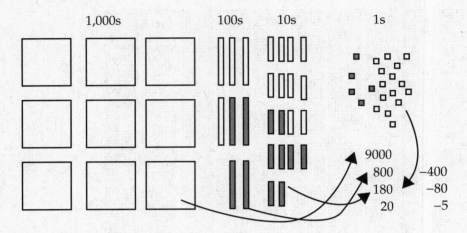

**Figure 1.3**   Isabel's sketch for 10,000 – 485.

Only one student, Brianne, used a number line and an adding-on    520
strategy to solve the problem (Figure 1.4). This really surprised me
because I knew that my students had used this approach a lot in
elementary school. I made note to be sure to have Brianne share her
approach when I pulled the whole group together for discussion.

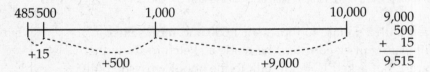

**Figure 1.4**   Brianne's number line and adding-on strategy.

With only about 15 minutes left in the period, I wanted to do some    525
whole-group sharing, particularly for the models that would be difficult
to discuss another day because of how long it had taken students to build
them. I decided, both because of the size of the models and the frequency
of the approach, to ask Emily, Ian, and Natalie to share first. Their model
was quite concrete, with paper grids of 100 arranged in a 10-by-10 array.    530
When I asked if anyone had solved the problem using the same method,
Griffin's table said they had solved it the same way, except instead of
cutting out paper hundreds grids, they had used the plastic base ten flats.
Their resulting 10-by-10 array of 10-by-10 flats almost completely covered
the table.    535

Next, I asked Marshall and Brie to talk about their method, which also represented a collection of 10,000. They had used graph paper, and their hundreds squares (which were smaller than the paper grids used by the first group) were arranged in a 5-by-20 grid.

At this point I asked the class to look at all the models we had seen and consider what is the same and what is different about them. Here are some of the ideas they listed:

- They all have 10,000 in them.

- Marshall and Brie's has smaller squares.

- Griffin's takes up a lot of space because it has big squares.

- If you got this in $20 bills, it wouldn't be as much, but it would be the same amount.

When I asked for clarification about the last observation, the student explained that $20s don't take up as much room as $1s, but it would still be the same amount of money. I commented, "I wonder what would happen if you got the money in dimes." This was not a problem to deal with today, but an interesting connection to the powers of ten within this problem.

Next, I asked Brianne to share her method. She explained that she had started with $485 and jumped to landmark numbers on the number line. "Start at $485 since he already spent it. It took 15 to get to 500 and would take another 500 to get to 1,000. Then I had to jump 9,000 to get from 1,000 to 10,000." I asked where she looked to find her answer, and Brianne said, "It's the number on the jumps, so 9,000 plus 500 plus 15, which is 9,515." I asked the class if there were questions about her approach, and there were none.

At the very end of the period, I asked the students to think about a method or model they might use if they found out that Uncle Marvin was really a millionaire. (He still planned to give you the money remaining after he bought the remote control wiener dog, if you could figure out how much that would be.) In the next lesson, we would look at their approaches to the extension problem and compare these to their representations of the original.

One student, Joe, had solved the original problem early, so I had given him the extension before the class period was up. Before he left, he showed me what he had done. His diagrams for both problems are shown in Figure 1.5. Joe commented that his new diagram is basically

## Olive

GRADE 6, SEPTEMBER

the same as the old one, except the shaded portion "is like a blown-up version of the triangle" in the corner of the second diagram. He justified this by saying, "If one square is now worth 1,000, the $485 is just a little bit less than one-half the square, so you can see the 999,515."

575

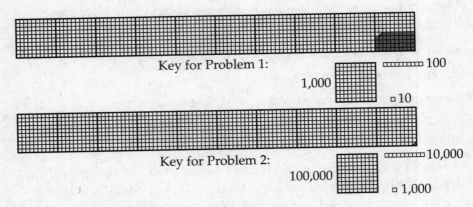

**Figure 1.5**   Joe's diagrams for 10,000 − 485 and 1,000,000 − 485.

Building a System of Tens

C H A P T E R

# 2

# The base ten structure of numbers

| CASE 6 | Number of days in school | Dawn, Kindergarten, December |
|---|---|---|
| CASE 7 | One hundred ninety-five | Danielle, Grade 1, April |
| CASE 8 | Who invented zero anyway? | Muriel, Grade 2, April |
| CASE 9 | Groups and leftovers | Donna, Grade 2, March |
| CASE 10 | Thinking with number lines | Leslie, Grade 6, September |
| CASE 11 | How many thousands in 437,812? | Susie, Grade 6, November |

In chapter 2, we continue to investigate students' understanding of how numbers are decomposed, but we take a step back for a different perspective. Rather than examine students who are working on computation, we consider students who are learning about how the components of a number relate to written numerals. It is easy for adults to see, for example, that the number 706 represents 7 hundreds, 0 tens, and 6 ones; or 6 hundreds, 10 tens, and 6 ones; or 70 tens and 6 ones, and so forth. However, when we study students who are in

29

the process of learning, we discover that these ideas are not so simple. As you read chapter 2, take notes on these issues:

- Some of the students in the cases offer incorrect answers. Look for elements of sound reasoning in their thinking. If the students are working from a logical position, where does their thinking go awry?

- In some of the cases, students discuss their own new insights. What are these insights, and how do they come about?

- How are the issues that sixth graders confront related to those of the primary-grade children? What new ideas about place value arise for the older students?

After reading the chapter, reread this introduction.

CASE 6

# Number of Days in School

## Dawn

KINDERGARTEN, DECEMBER

Each morning, as my kindergarten class gathers on the meeting rug, we run through a routine that helps set our day in motion. This set of rituals includes taking attendance, working with our classroom calendar and weather graph, and recording how many days we have been in school. It is amazing how much mathematics is involved in these activities, and often I am astounded by the thoughtful responses five- and six-year-olds give to such questions as, "What number should we record on our days-in-school chart today?" This morning, our sixtieth day of school, we turned to our days-in-school chart.

Over the years, I have spent a lot of time thinking about the optimal way to record this data with kindergarten students. Many years ago I used a number line that spanned the top of the chalkboard, but found that this was too physically removed from the children, not to mention extremely cumbersome for me. Having seen in the past the merits of

5

10

Building a System of Tens

using hundreds boards when working with older students, I wondered
if this type of grid might have a place in the kindergarten classroom
as well. About ten years ago I made a switch to this type of recording
system for tracking how many days we have been in school each year.
Every day I record the number on our 10-by-18 grid, and the child who
is the calendar-helper adds one seashell to a cup that we keep nearby.
This provides a set of concrete objects that corresponds to the number
being logged on the chart. From time to time, the children count this set
of shells, and we then compare our two types of recording systems to
connect the quantity of shells with the number we count, read, and write.
If necessary, we then adjust our data.

| 1 | 2 | 3 | 4 | 5 | 6 | 7 | 8 | 9 | 10 |
|---|---|---|---|---|---|---|---|---|---|
| 11 | 12 | 13 | 14 | 15 | 16 | 17 | 18 | 19 | 20 |
| 21 | 22 | 23 | 24 | 25 | 26 | 27 | 28 | 29 | 30 |
| 31 | 32 | 33 | 34 | 35 | 36 | 37 | 38 | 39 | 40 |
| 41 | 42 | 43 | 44 | 45 | 46 | 47 | 48 | 49 | 50 |
| 51 | 52 | 53 | 54 | 55 | 56 | 57 | 58 | 59 | |
| | | | | | | | | | |
| | | | | | | | | | |
| | | | | | | | | | |

To begin our discussion this morning, I asked, "What number should I
write on our chart today?" Hands shot up and I began writing responses
on the chalkboard next to our chart, hoping to allow as many children
as possible to respond before recording the "right answer" on the grid.
Often this type of discussion yields some interesting discoveries. Today
was no exception.

ANDREW:     I think it's fifty-ten. [*I wrote 510 on the board.*]

JOSEF:      Sixty. [*I wrote 60.*]

More hands shot up, and Bianca, Jared, Rhea, Terry, Toshi, Pat, John, Sione, Susan, and Brady all responded "Sixty." Some children added other comments, too.

TOSHI:       I know it's 60. I just know it is.

Jared, John, and Sione were equally emphatic. Susan seemed a little less sure, but apparently wanted to go along with the general consensus. Still more responses kept coming as more hands were up.

TAMIKA:      Forty. [*I wrote 40.*]

JERREL:      Eight. [*I wrote 8.*]

NINA:        Seventy. [*I wrote 70.*]

"How can we find out which number we should write today?" I asked, to continue our discussion.

BIANCA:      Counting, so we could know what comes next.

JOSEF:       All the numbers are in front of it, 'cause 6 comes after 5, you know.

As Josef spoke, he moved up to the chart and pointed to the column of numbers on the right hand side, stopping at the empty box under the 50.

JARED:       Yeah, see, zero all the way down.

ANDREW:      Don't forget the 10.

Once again, physical involvement seemed a necessity as Andrew moved up to the chart and dragged his finger across the row with the numbers 51, 52, 53, 54, 55, 56, 57, 58, and 59. Andrew seemed to be making use of the number (counting) sequence; thus his response of "fifty-ten" (510) made perfect sense.

BRADY:       But it's a 6. [*Again, moving up to point at the chart, Brady's finger slid down the right hand column just as Toshi's and Jared's had as they spoke.*] See, 1, 2, 3, 4, 5, and 6 goes here 'cause you're counting down.

TOSHI:       See, it's 60. I know it is.

Building a System of Tens

## Dawn

Sitting toward the back of the group was Norman. Though he didn't speak out in front of the group, my aide was taking notes and later related to me that he was making comments under his breath.

NORMAN: It can't be 8. We already had that one. . . . Fifty-ten looks like five hundred and ten. That is too big to go there.

Because we needed to move on, I ended this discussion by reminding the children that another way to check was to use Bianca's suggested strategy of counting. Together, as I pointed to each number on our chart, we counted from 1 to 60 and agreed that 60 was the number to be written in the box for today. As we finished, there were two final comments:

JOSEF: Are we going to get 100?

BRADY: Yes, 'cause look, we can count by tens: 10, 20, 30, 40, 50, 60. I think we will get to more than 100.

As I reflect on these events, I am particularly taken by the ease with which some children are able to connect to the systematic way we use numbers. At the same time, I know for sure that not all children in my class are making sense of this experience at this time. Trying to provide opportunities where young children can investigate numbers in a meaningful way is a challenge.

C A S E  7

# One hundred and ninety-five

## Danielle

In my classroom we do work on estimation, which gives the children experience in making reasonable guesses as well as the opportunity to count objects. Last week, we were working with a bag of jelly beans. The students were trying to guess how many jelly beans they could hold in one hand, and then compared that to the actual amount they could hold.

# Danielle

We also discussed whether the amount would be the same every time they took a handful. Then we estimated the amount of beans in the whole bag. After we all made our predictions, I opened the bag and spread the jelly beans on a flat surface, to give the children the chance to decide if they were satisfied with their estimate, to adjust it if needed, and to say if it was too high or too low.

The children in my class had not done any formal work with place value, although we had counted objects well beyond 100. Several times students had asked how to write a number greater than 100 and I had showed them. But as of yet, we hadn't discussed numbers containing three digits. As we finished up with the jelly-bean counting, we learned that the bag contained a total of 195 jelly beans. I asked if anyone knew how to write that number using numerals. Suggestions included the following:

1095

10095

195

1395

1295

The children who gave the first two responses were able to explain them somewhat. They heard "hundred" and remembered something about 100 and zeros. They couldn't be more specific than that. Nathan, who gave the third response, said 195 looked like that and he just knew it. The child who gave the fourth response said it was a big number and that's how you write big numbers. The child who gave the fifth response, Bethany, responded the same as the Nathan. (She usually repeats an answer after hearing someone else give it.)

I asked the children to look at these numbers, think about 195, and talk to each other about it. I also said that one of these was the right way to write it with numerals.

The children explained their answers to each other and arrived at the conclusion that the correct written form is 195. I don't recall the entire discussion, but I do remember that 1395 and 1295 were immediately discarded because they never heard anything about 3 or 2 in the number.

Building a System of Tens

Nathan, who was the first one to offer 195, was able to convince everyone that he was right, which, of course, he was. I was curious about how he knew this.

When I suggested to Nathan that we spend some one-on-one time discussing how he knew about 195, he was more than pleased to spend the time with me alone. As we sat down together, he was all smiles and wanted to show me how smart he was.

TEACHER: Show me how to write one hundred ninety-five. [*Nathan writes 195.*] Why this way?

NATHAN: I first thought it was [*writes*] 1095, but that would be ten hundred ninety-five.

TEACHER: Why?

NATHAN: Take away the 95 and the 1 and 0 is ten.

TEACHER: What made you think of writing 195?

NATHAN: When I see 100 and go up, you take away the zeros. When you go up 100, 101, 102, you keep going up. You take away the zeros.

TEACHER: Why do you do that?

NATHAN: If you don't take away the zeros it would be 10095. That would be 100 and 95 put on the end.

TEACHER: How do you know about numbers?

NATHAN: I can count up to 500. [*Starts to count, says 49, 30, self-corrects to 50, 51 . . . At 235, I ask him to stop.*]

TEACHER: When you look at 195 [*I write 195*], what do the parts tell you?

NATHAN: [*Makes circles around the numbers.*] Nineteen—if you take away the 5, just plain 5. If you take away the 19 [*he writes 195 again and circles parts of it*], 95 or 19. The middle can go either way. Plain 1, if you take away the 95, says "hundred."

TEACHER:     Can you write other numbers? [*I dictate the numbers 372, 249,* 150
             *107, 950, and 401, and Nathan transcribes them this way: 372,*
             *249, 1007, 950, 4011. Then he changes 4011 to 401, but doesn't*
             *comment on or change 1007.*]

I wish I understood better how to interpret what Nathan knew.
It appeared that he had some initial thoughts about place value.      155
For example, he saw that numbers have different values in different
situations. How much did he understand about these values? A few
weeks later, we were working with base ten blocks. Nathan was trying to
figure out how many days were in summer. He knew right away that 30
was three rods. But in trying to add the days in June, July, and August,  160
he needed to add 30, 31, and 31. He didn't use tens as he counted, but
instead counted each individual space on the tens rod. Where do he and
I go from here?

C A S E  8

# Who invented zero anyway?

## Muriel

My second graders and I were looking at the hundreds chart set up in
a 10-by-10 array. I had imagined leading a discussion toward the idea      165
that moving down one space is actually adding 10. As we got into the
discussion, I found that it is, of course, a complicated idea; even if I just
tell my students that it works this way, they don't "get it" in any kind
of meaningful way. Besides that, several of my students raised a very
different idea—an idea about their understanding of zero. Following is a    170
portion of our discussion.

# Muriel

| 1 | 2 | 3 | 4 | 5 | 6 | 7 | 8 | 9 | 10 |
|---|---|---|---|---|---|---|---|---|-----|
| 11 | 12 | 13 | 14 | 15 | 16 | 17 | 18 | 19 | 20 |
| 21 | 22 | 23 | 24 | 25 | 26 | 27 | 28 | 29 | 30 |
| 31 | 32 | 33 | 34 | 35 | 36 | 37 | 38 | 39 | 40 |
| 41 | 42 | 43 | 44 | 45 | 46 | 47 | 48 | 49 | 50 |
| 51 | 52 | 53 | 54 | 55 | 56 | 57 | 58 | 59 | 60 |
| 61 | 62 | 63 | 64 | 65 | 66 | 67 | 68 | 69 | 70 |
| 71 | 72 | 73 | 74 | 75 | 76 | 77 | 78 | 79 | 80 |
| 81 | 82 | 83 | 84 | 85 | 86 | 87 | 88 | 89 | 90 |
| 91 | 92 | 93 | 94 | 95 | 96 | 97 | 98 | 99 | 100 |

Beth is describing for me—and anyone who is listening—why it works to move down one and actually add ten on this particular hundreds chart.

BETH:      See the nines? [*She points to the column of 9, 19, 29, 39 . . .*] This is 0 + 9, 10 + 9, 20 + 9, 30 + 9. The difference between 50 and 60 is 10, so the difference between 59 and 69 is 10.

Quite articulate, I think. Then Beth continues.

BETH:      [*She points to 45.*] This has 4 tens and one 5. These [*pointing to the columns with numbers ending in 6 or 7*] all have sixes, sevens. [*Now she points to the 10, 20, 30 column.*] This one has zeros. But these aren't quite zero, because. . . .

Her voice kind of trails off and my mind is racing. What did she say? "These aren't quite zero"?

TEACHER:      Because why? [*I am trying desperately to figure out in that moment all of what she is saying and trying to sort out what I might ask next.*]

| BETH: | Because if zero isn't here [*she points to 60*], then this 6 is only 6. It depends on where it [the zero] is. See, 15. [*She writes 15 on the board.*] This [*points to the 1*] is a 10, not a 1. Ten has everything in it up to 9. The ten section has from 10 to 99. The hundred section has—say it's one hundred and twenty-five. [*She writes 125 on the board.*] But you don't write it as 100 or else it would look like this. [*She writes 100205 on the board.*] | 190 |

I'm in that place where I find myself spending a lot of time: hearing many rich ideas, and wondering which ideas I should push on. I decide to push on Beth's ideas about the zero thing.

195

| TEACHER: | You've written 125 separately, as 100205. But tell me some more about zero. | |

| BETH: | It is sort of zero, but not exactly. [In 30] this zero makes it be 30. If this zero weren't there, it'd be 3. | 200 |

| YESSICA: | I have something to say about how these zeros aren't really zeros. | |

Attempting to include some other children in the discussion, I restate what Beth has said, about the zero at the end of the number not being quite the same as zero by itself. Yessica comes up to the board.

205

| YESSICA: | [*Writing 07 on the board*] That's 7. [*Now writes 0.7*] That's 0 point 7. [*And then she writes 70.*] That's 70. Zero represents 7 tens. | |

I am completely intrigued by these ideas and love the term *represents*.

210

| TEACHER: | So if this zero [*pointing to 0 in 70*] represents tens, in this number, 79, does the 9 represent tens? | |

| BETH: | Do you know what we really mean? Do you know the real thing? | |

Lately Beth has been responding to my questions as if I did already know many of the answers I'm asking her to explain to me. I like to make my questioning as authentic as I can, but the fact is that I usually understand the mathematics that I'm asking the children to think

215

Building a System of Tens

through. Today my questions are framed to find out what the children are thinking, to hear their ideas. I know that the 9 in 79 represents 9 ones, but I'm not sure what Beth thinks.

I explain to her that in my math class for adults, we've talked a lot about zero and what it means to different people, and what it's worth, and whether it's odd or even, for example. And I express my honest interest in what second graders think about zero. This is heard by several other people in class and they perk up a bit. The discussion continues.

YESSICA:      On the calculator there's a 07.

TEACHER:      And then is the 0 worth zero?

YESSICA:      Yes. [*Other children nod in agreement.*]

TEACHER:      But not in the 70?

YESSICA:      Right.

BRIAN:        For just 7, the zero doesn't have to be there, just the 7.

LAMONT:       There are two ways to make zero. This is the 7 for the tens and it [the zero] makes 70.

TEACHER:      What's the other kind of zero?

LAMONT:       For the ones. [*He writes 08.*]

I'm thinking, "Two kinds of zeros? Wow."

BETH:         It's like you sort of understand it, but nobody really understands it. Maybe someone will come around and figure it out. And who invented zero anyway?

I laugh and write the question on the board.

WENONA:       Yeah, and who invented numbers anyway?

I write this down on the board also.

TEACHER:      I need to see if I can find any information for you to read.

Several days later Lamont came with delight on his face to tell me that our librarian had seen the questions on the board and said she had a book called *Zero Is Not Nothing* (Sitomer, 1978). He eagerly went to the library to bring it back.

The next week, Henry came to me and said sincerely, "You see, Ms. Willis," holding his hands closed and then opening them palms up, "zero means there's nothing. See, there's nothing in my hands. That means zero." 250

I was thrilled that he had actually kept this issue in his head long enough to either talk to someone about it, or come up with that explanation on his own. It was also somehow very touching to me 255 that he seemed to be gently offering me an explanation about something I didn't yet understand.

I guess I've written up this episode for a couple of reasons. One is simply that I love the idea that even a few of my second graders can have this kind of discussion about number. This kind of "chewing" on ideas is 260 exactly what I most hope and work for in my mathematics (actually any subject) class. I am genuinely intrigued to have this window into some second graders' thinking about what zero is. I also am thrilled that the assertion is in the air that someone invented this zero thing, as well as the particular numbers that we use. It makes them much more accessible and 265 "touchable."

I also wonder how making sense of zero affects children's understanding of place value. Actually, it's probably more to the point to wonder how *not* making sense of zero affects children's understanding of place value. 270

I am sometimes just overwhelmed with the range of ideas that bombard me in a relatively short discussion.

CASE 9

# Groups and leftovers

## Donna

GRADE 2, MARCH

At the beginning of March, I was trying to decide how to introduce place value. My goal was to help the children develop an understanding of how our number system works so that they would have a solid foundation 275 when we began to work on adding and subtracting that involved regrouping. I decided there were two paths I could follow: I could set up some activities that would guide the children to make certain observations and connections, or I could start with word problems and work from there. Unfortunately, I didn't feel completely comfortable with either route. The activities that guided the children toward a particular end seemed too planned and constrained, and I wasn't comfortable spending a lot of time on these. On the other hand, I felt there were really important concepts about place value that might not surface if I didn't set up the situation for it to happen. So I decided to compromise. We would set the stage with one activity that focused on grouping tens and proceed from there.

I adapted an activity I had seen in Van de Walle's *Elementary School Mathematics: Teaching Developmentally* (1990). My version asks the children to take a handful of kidney beans (less than 100—we had practiced eyeballing 100 beans on our hundredth day of school) and count them, filling in the information in a table that started like this:

| Number in group | Whole groups | Leftovers | How many all together |
|---|---|---|---|
| 7 | | | |
| 3 | | | |
| 6 | | | |

The verbal instructions asked the children to put each new handful of beans into groups of whatever number was in the first column. For example, if the number in the first column was 7, they had to put their beans into groups of 7 and then fill in the rest of the information. I had chosen a variety of numbers to go in that first column, but I made sure that 10 appeared at least three times near the end of the sheet. The planned outcome was that the children would notice a pattern when they put the beans into full groups of 10—a pattern that didn't occur with any other number. I put the children into pairs and they set off to work.

As I circulated through the room, I noticed that the children were using several different strategies to accomplish their task. Kathy counted all the beans by ones. Jelani put the beans into groups and then counted, while Ellen decided to "make sure" and check Jelani's work by counting their beans again. Marc and Karla seemed to enjoy the challenge of taking more than 100 beans and were discussing their outcomes.

# Donna

Amy and Tuan were the first group I heard remark about the pattern they saw in the tens rows. They were discussing the fact that the number of whole groups and the number of leftovers turned out to be the number of beans that they had all together—that the number in the last column was a combination of the numbers in the previous two columns. At this point I also heard Kathy, who has a keen eye for patterns, make a similar observation.

| Number in group | Whole groups | Leftovers | How many all together |
|---|---|---|---|
| 3 | 7 | 2 | 23 |
| 7 | 5 | 5 | 40 |
| 10 | 6 | 7 | 67 |
| 10 | 3 | 8 | 38 |

The next day, the children finished their work and we came together to put our findings on a whole-class chart. The children offered examples of how to fill each line of the chart, and then I asked if they saw anything on the chart that they wanted to comment on. Many kids noticed what they came to call "the ten trick." I asked them why it worked.

Kimberly tried to explain what she understood: "The tens is what basically does it and the leftovers make it." Several other children tried to explain what seemed to be clear and yet confusing at the same time.

Eventually I asked, "Will it work with any other number of things in a group?" I expected their answer would be no, thinking only about groups of 10 and fewer, but I heard something different as the discussion continued.

Sean stated that he thought this "trick" would work with anything that had a 10 in it. I wasn't sure just what Sean meant, but several other children began to think about his comment and offered their ideas. Marc said that anything with a "one-zero" at the beginning would work. Sean responded that it worked with a hundred, a thousand, ten thousand, and a million.

Ellen said, "Fourteen groups of ten might not work." Most of the class agreed with this statement, but they weren't completely sure, so we all decided to test it. We took 14 groups of beans with 10 in each group, and I threw in a few leftovers. The children counted the groups by tens, and as we approached 140 the excitement mounted. I recorded our results on the chart and the class was abuzz.

Jelani said out loud, "Why does that work?"

Building a System of Tens

Throughout the discussion, I was thinking about some of the ideas that had come up the week before while we were doing some mental math (arithmetic in our heads). The children had stated the following theory: "Ten plus any number less than 10 and more than 2 is a teen that has the same number at the end." Now I reminded them of their theory and asked if there was a connection between what we were seeing on this chart and that statement.

340

345

Marc's answer seemed to sum up my thoughts about teaching place value. He said, "There is a big connection, but I can't explain it."

C A S E **10**

# Thinking with number lines

*Leslie*
GRADE 6, SEPTEMBER

Each year, I begin with a similar goal: to pose mathematical tasks that require my sixth-grade students to use different models to represent and explain their problem solving strategies. Some students come to our middle school from classrooms with similar expectations and experiences, but for many, explaining and representing their ideas this way is a new challenge.

350

Our class begins with a daily warm-up, and I thought this might be a good way to get students thinking about the relative size of numbers on a number line. Both confident and struggling students have limited experience with number lines, so I expected to both probe understandings and uncover misconceptions. I posed the following question:

355

Where would you place 375 on this number line? Explain how you decide where it is located.

360

0                                              10, 0000

## Leslie

During warm-ups, students are given time to write about their ideas in their notebooks, and then they share with their table partners. What follows is what I saw and heard as I moved around the room to view their work, listen to their conversations, and decide what ideas to bring to the whole group for discussion.

Lucas and Jake both started by marking 5,000 in the middle (Figures 2.1 and 2.2). I listened to their conversation.

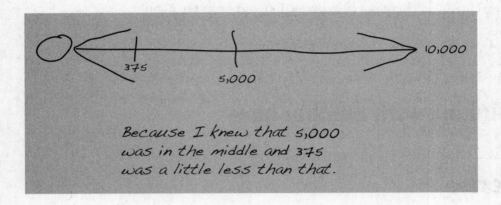

**Figure 2.1**   Lucas's diagram and explanation.

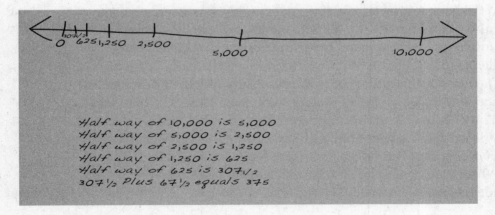

**Figure 2.2**   Jake's diagram and explanation.

Building a System of Tens

LUCAS:     Well, I knew 5,000 was half of 10,000, so that's why it is in the middle. Then I put 375 between 0 and 5,000 because I knew that 375 was less than 5,000 and more than zero.     370

JAKE:      How did you know where to put it? I mean, I know it's less than 5,000, but how much less?

Lucas:     I didn't really think about that.

JAKE:      Well, if you look at my number line, you can see that I started with 5,000 like you did. Then I only had half of the number line to worry about.     375

Lucas:     What do you mean? You have the whole number line like I do.

JAKE:      Yeah, but once I knew where 5,000 was, I didn't think about this half of the number line again [*pointing to the side greater than 5,000*]. I only looked at this half [*indicates the side less than 5,000*] because I knew 375 would be in this half somewhere, I just didn't know where yet. So I kept cutting it in half until I got really close to 375, and that's how I decided where it went.     380

I moved on to Tyrese and Anthony.     385

TYRESE:    Well, I knew that 5,000 would be in the middle, so I put it there. Then I thought about how I could divide up the part between 0 and 5,000 so it would be easier to see where 375 would go, since 375 isn't easy. So I decided I would put 1,000, 2,000, 3,000, and 4,000 on the number line. And then I knew where 375 would go.     390

ANTHONY:   OK, I get what you did. I did it a different way. I started at the 0 and counted by 50s until I got to 400. I knew 375 would be halfway between 350 and 400. Then I thought that my number line would have to be a lot longer, because the way it was, 400 was too close to 10,000, so I added all of these lines to show that it would be far away.     395

# Leslie

GRADE 6, SEPTEMBER

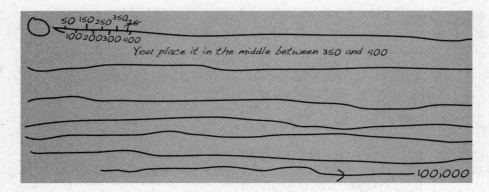

50  150 250 350 75
100 200 300 400

You place it in the middle between 350 and 400

100,000

**Figure 2.3**  Anthony's extended number line.

TYRESE:    Are you allowed to move 10,000?

ANTHONY:   Well, I had to move it, or it would be wrong.

Shaquille and Chris were talking about how their number lines were
similar.

SHAQUILLE: Ours look the same at the beginning. Your numbers are by
           hundreds, and so are mine, if you look at the numbers on
           the bottom. After I finished with hundreds, I went back and
           added fifties in between and you didn't. I stopped when I
           got to 1,000, but if I had kept going, ours would have been
           almost the same.

CHRIS:     I kept going to 10,000 because it's supposed to have numbers
           all the way across. It has to be all divided up all the way
           across.

SHAQUILLE: I think if we put yours and mine next to each other, where
           we have 375 would match.

# Leslie

GRADE 6, SEPTEMBER

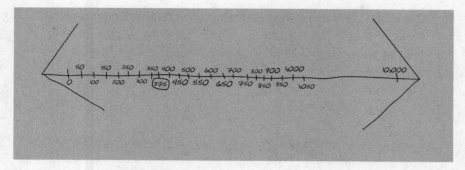

**Figure 2.4**  Shaquille's number line.

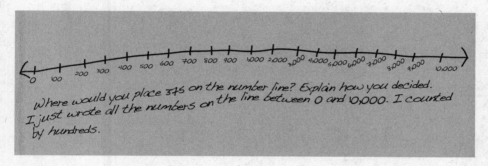

**Figure 2.5**  Chris's number line.

Olivia explained what she was thinking about as she got started on the task. She constructed several number lines (Figure 2.6).

OLIVIA:     Well, at first I thought that 375 was hard to start with, so I        415
            asked myself what would be an easier number to start with,
            and I decided 500. Then I thought some more, and I realized
            it would have to be 5,000, not 500, because it's 10,000 instead
            of 1,000.

TEACHER:    I'm not sure what you mean. Can you tell us why you were           420
            thinking about 500 and 5,000?

OLIVIA:     Well, I was confused at first, because I thought 500 would
            be an easy number to put on the number line. I was

Chapter 2

47

# Leslie

GRADE 6, SEPTEMBER

thinking it would go in the middle. Then when I got ready
to write it down, I saw that it should be 5,000 instead of
500, because 5,000 is half of 10,000. It's a 10,000 on the
end of the number line, not a 1,000. That's why I changed
my mind.

425

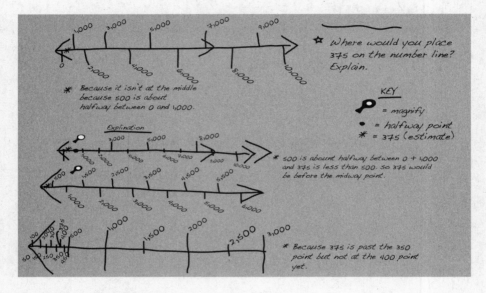

**Figure 2.6** Olivia's number lines.

Now that I see the work students did individually and in pairs, I need
to think through what has been revealed about what my students
do and do not understand. Once I think that through, I can decide
which ideas I want the class to consider in whole group. Which students
should I ask to present their number lines, and what questions should I
pose about them?

430

Building a System of Tens

# How many thousands in 437,812?

## *Susie*

As a math coach, I have been working with teachers and students in
lower grades, and I know how difficult it can be for students to acquire
an understanding of place value. Because of this work, I have been
wondering about older students. Do they struggle with place value issues
as well? I recently had an opportunity to explore these questions when
a sixth-grade teacher invited me into her classroom. We agreed that I
would teach the lesson while she observed, and then we would discuss
what we learned.

    In order to find out more about student understanding of place value,
I wrote the following numbers, each on a separate card:

        437,812

      6,437,812

   36,437,812

  536,437,812

1,536,437,812

    I started the lesson by holding up the card for the first number.
I asked the students if they could tell me the number. Students
responded by raising their hands, appearing confident and anxious to
share. I asked Rachel if she would read the number, which she was able
to do without error.

TEACHER: How did you know this was four hundred thirty-seven
thousand, eight hundred twelve?

RACHEL: Because of the commas!

TEACHER: What do you mean, "because of the commas"?

RACHEL:     The commas break the numbers up, and each part has a
            different name.                                              460

When asked, Rachel explained that "each part" referred to thousands,
millions, billions, and so forth. In her explanation, Rachel traced the
comma with her finger while saying *thousand*. She described picturing the
number in her mind like this:

437 , 812

Most students were able to identify the numbers correctly. During       465
our discussion, I asked several questions to confirm that the students
could *read and write numerals to one billion*, as required by our state core
curriculum. When the numbers became increasingly more difficult, I
wondered what processes the students were using to correctly identify
the number.                                                              470

TEACHER:    What were you thinking when you read the number?

GABRIELLA:  I memorized the columns for place values and I know that 5
            is in the hundred millions column. I was following a pattern.

TEACHER:    [*holding up the card for 1,536,437,812*] What about this
            number?                                                      475

TRINIA:     I know that number, it's one trillion, five hundred thirty-six
            million, four hundred thirty-seven thousand, eight hundred
            twelve. Wait, I forgot the billions.

TEACHER:    When you said trillion, what were you thinking?

TRINIA:     I just got mixed up which place the trillion goes into.       480

Trinia's comments were typical. I continued to question how the
students determined "which place" they were working with in each
number. Proceeding with the lesson, I asked class to look at 437,812 and

find how many thousands are in this number. I told the students to think about it for a few minutes and then work with their partners. As they began this task, I walked around the room, listening to their ideas.

485

MIKE: I think there are 3.

ALI: Maybe 4.

MIKE: I think it might be 3 because we have 4 hundred 37 thousand; I think 3 might be the right answer.

490

ANNA: I think it's 1 thousand, because this [*pointing*] is the hundred thousand place, and this is the ten thousand place, and this is the one thousand place. I think it's 1.

TRENT: What makes this hard is that there is a 4 in the hundred thousand place and a 3 in the ten thousand place and a 7 in the thousand place. All three numbers are in the space for thousands.

495

ALI: I think it's 4 or 3 or 7. I don't know for sure, but if you turn all of these numbers to zero [*referring to 812*], this is what you have left.

500

MIKE: I know why the 3 is the right answer! I looked at the number and I saw these are in the thousands place because I knew this is the ones, tens, and hundreds. I knew that these were the thousands, so I looked at it and saw that there were three numbers in the thousands place. So there are 3 thousands in that number.

505

The students were struggling more than I had anticipated. They seemed to have a limited understanding of place value. They had learned the name of the place of each digit, but did not understand the value or the relationship of the digits within a number. Why is place value such a difficult concept to grasp? As I pondered this question, I moved to the next group. They stopped their conversation as I approached.

510

TEACHER: What do you think the answer is?

TRINIA: We think it's 250.

TEACHER: Tell me about your thinking.

515

CHASE: Each of these [*referring to each digit in the number*] have 10, so we just times'd each number by 10. Then added the numbers together.

TEACHER: I think I understand why you chose to multiply each number by 10, but I'm not sure. Will you explain it to me? | 520

MAGGIE: Each number is 10 times the other number.

TEACHER: Does that mean there are 10 tens in one hundred?

MAGGIE: YES!

TEACHER: Then how many tens are in one thousand?

CHASE: Uh-oh. | 525

TEACHER: What do you mean, Chase?

CHASE: We forgot that each number has to have all of the other numbers times'd.

TEACHER: How will this help you find how many thousands are in our number? | 530

TRINIA: I not sure, but we need to keep working on it.

Although these students still have quite a lot to sort out, I was encouraged to see that they started to make connections between the values of the digits. Now that they seemed to have a more productive direction to pursue, I moved on to the next group. | 535

SADIE: I think it's just 37 thousand.

TEACHER: Why do you think that?

SADIE: Because the 4 means hundred thousand, but the 37 just sticks together and makes 37 thousands.

TEACHER: Do you mean 37 groups of one thousand, or do you mean 37 thousand? | 540

SADIE: I think 37 thousand, but I'm not sure.

MEAGAN: I think all we have to do is divide.

JUAN: What do you mean?

Building a System of Tens

MEAGAN:     If we want to know how many things are in a number, you just divide. It's like if you have a number, let's say 100, and you want to know how many 5s are in the number, you have to divide to figure it out.

JUAN:       OK, you divide; I'm not going to divide that number!

The students in this group retrieved their calculators and determined there were 437.812 thousands in 437,812.

I found this teaching experience to be quite revealing. Although the students can read and write numbers to one billion, as specified in our state framework, they seem to be missing many ideas about the base ten structure of numbers. Now I must prepare a meeting with the teacher to discuss what her students understand, what her students still need to learn, and what would be fruitful next steps for her class.

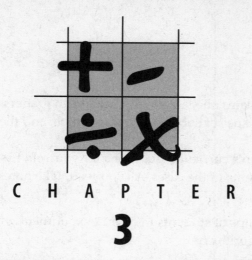

C H A P T E R
# 3

# Making sense of addition and subtraction algorithms

| CASE 12 | The pink way | *Lynn, Grade 2, May* |
|---|---|---|
| CASE 13 | Subtraction and invented algorithms | *Lynn, Grade 2, April (one year later)* |
| CASE 14 | Partitioning subtraction problems | *Nadine, Grade 4, February* |

Over the last several years, Lynn, a second-grade teacher, has been thinking hard about the issues explored in chapters 1 and 2. As she tries to sort out what her second graders need to learn, and as she reviews what she has done in different years, she poses big curricular questions for herself. What do second graders need to learn about adding, subtracting, and place value? What kinds of mathematical tasks will help them learn these things? And what is the role of the standard algorithms conventionally taught in the United States? In the first of these two cases, Lynn reviews what she has done in her first two years of teaching second grade and shares her current thoughts. In the second case, written one year later, she has different ideas.

In case 14, Nadine relates one lesson with her fourth graders in which she, too, is addressing issues of subtraction, place value, and the U.S. standard algorithm.

Before taking on Lynn's curricular questions for yourself, first examine the thinking of the students in the cases. As you read, take notes on these questions:

- How do the two groups of students in case 12 experiment with different addition algorithms?

- In case 13, consider second grader Fiona's work: Where does she get stuck, and how does she sort herself out?

- In case 14, in what ways are Hallie's and Janet's subtraction procedures the same and how are they different?

C A S E  **12**

# The pink way

## Lynn
GRADE 2, MAY

As the end of my second year of teaching second grade approaches, I find myself consumed, again, with questions about what the children are thinking when they add and subtract with regrouping. These questions seem broad and deep, and range from the level of the individual child—"What *is* he thinking?"—to the level of math education in the United States—"What is the role of traditional algorithms when the focus of teaching is on student understanding?"

Last year, I used trading games (chip-trading and rods-trading) to get at the issues I thought were involved in regrouping. I taught the children how to play (roll the dice, take tens rods and ones rods to correspond to your roll, and represent your accumulating total with rods), making sure they knew to trade in 10 ones for a ten and 10 tens for a hundred. Later,

I gave them word problems that involved regrouping, thinking they would apply their new knowledge to solve them. I was dismayed to discover that very few, if any, children made the connection between trading in ones rods for tens rods and adding two-digit numbers when the ones columns totaled more than 10. Some of them did learn the algorithm—I think because they were able to remember the steps and wanted to do as they were told.

I am not convinced that any of them really understood how quantities combine. Some of the children did not learn the procedure, despite an obvious desire to do well and please their teacher. Some children, when faced with a problem that involved regrouping, just stopped. Some added on, counting by ones. Some ignored the dilemma of having, for example, 15 in the ones column, and came up with solutions that did not make sense.

This November I taught the rods-trading game again. I did not dare *not* to. I was determined to find an effective way to help the children *connect* the game to the addition it is meant to represent.

It did not work. Every way I thought of to make the connection clear was so confusing to the children that they could not even understand how to "do" the paper, much less say, "Oh! This adding is just like rods-trading!" or "Oh! This rods-trading is the same thing as adding!" It was frustrating for me and bewildering for the children.

A significant difference this year was that I included lots of word problems along with rods-trading throughout the whole year. I did not try to get the children to use the algorithm to solve the problems, and I did not try to push the connection to rods-trading. Instead, I asked children how they solved the word problems—since they all did—and recorded their procedures on audio tape and on posters.

Rods-trading had no discernible impact on how the children thought about addition and subtraction problems. Some children, who could answer questions about how many tens, how many ones, location of the tens and ones, and so on, would still count by ones when solving two-digit addition problems. Those children who apparently had a deeper understanding of place value still added the way they always had: tens first, and then the ones. They would occasionally use the words *trade in* to describe how they dealt with

having more than 10 ones. Some children could not answer questions    50
about where the tens and ones were, or did not understand what
counting by tens really meant.

For a while, we left trading games and regrouping as a topic and
worked on other things. Our math topics for the next several months
included geometry and many, many word problems.                        55

Then it was May and I felt the need to revisit the algorithm somehow.
My thinking went something like this: Third grade approacheth. It is not
up to me to say that we will all abandon the conventional algorithm. The
children will be expected to know it. If I don't teach it to them, someone
else will, perhaps wondering why I didn't do my job, which means now     60
they have to, and now they're way behind, and the kids will test poorly
the next year in fourth grade.

At some point I would like to have a discussion with my colleagues
about the algorithm and the ways kids solve problems. I fantasize that
we will all agree that children should be encouraged to think flexibly and  65
solve problems in ways that make sense to them and in ways that they
can explain without saying, "and then you do this because my teacher
said to."

Meanwhile, I am still facing the end-of-year dilemma over the
algorithm, so last week I prepared to approach addition with             70
regrouping again. I made a poster showing five different methods of
adding 38 and 25, each method written in a different color. The first four
were methods that second graders had articulated when explaining their
thinking in November; three of these (the green way, blue way, and red
way) involved adding the tens first. The purple way showed counting     75
on from 38 by ones. And, finally, the poster showed the traditional
algorithm, in pink.

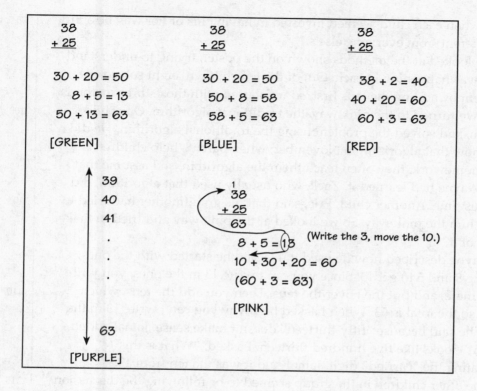

| | | |
|---|---|---|
| 38 | 38 | 38 |
| + 25 | + 25 | + 25 |
| | | |
| 30 + 20 = 50 | 30 + 20 = 50 | 38 + 2 = 40 |
| 8 + 5 = 13 | 50 + 8 = 58 | 40 + 20 = 60 |
| 50 + 13 = 63 | 58 + 5 = 63 | 60 + 3 = 63 |
| [GREEN] | [BLUE] | [RED] |

39
40
41
.
.
.

63

[PURPLE]

```
    1
   38
 + 25
   63
```
8 + 5 = 13   (Write the 3, move the 10.)
10 + 30 + 20 = 60
(60 + 3 = 63)

[PINK]

I met with a group of ten children who could solve regrouping problems pretty easily. I gave them the following word problem, asking them to pay attention to how they solved it and to please write something that would explain their thinking.

**?** Ms. Kosaka and Ms. Rivest were watching kids playing outside. They counted 38 children in and around the climbing structure. They saw 25 kids playing freeze tag on the field. How many kids did they see?

The children got right to work and solved the problem quickly. They were eager to explain their thinking, anticipating what I usually ask them to do. They seemed slightly miffed that, no, I did not want to hear their ideas right off; I wanted to show them something first. However, when I told them that I had listened to a tape of second graders explaining their thinking earlier in the year, in order to make a poster of different ways kids solve problems, they felt sufficiently represented to listen. When I showed them the poster, they excitedly said, "I did it that way!" or "I solved it the green way!" This was actually a change from earlier in the

80

85

90

year, when each child seemed invested in having his or her way be a little
bit different from everyone else's.

We looked at the methods shown on the poster, trying to understand
what was happening in each. Out of the ten children, eight solved the
problem by adding the tens first, so we started with those three methods.
Then we turned to the pink way, the traditional algorithm. One child,
Wayne, had solved the problem using the traditional algorithm. He did
not know that algorithm in November; when parents help children
with homework, they often teach them the algorithm, so I assume that's
how Wayne had learned it. Zack, who usually used that algorithm, did
not this time. Another child, Eric, said that his grandmother had tried to
show him the pink way. So we looked at the pink way and tried to make
sense of it.

Wayne described how he used it. He said he started with the ones,
adding 8 and 5 to get 13. Since you can't write 13 in the ones, you write
the 3 there, and put the 1 over the tens. Then you add the tens, which
is 60, so the total is 63. When I asked him why you can't write 13 in the
ones, he said because "fifty-thirteen" doesn't make sense. Jamal added
that 513 looks like five hundred thirteen. I asked, "What is this 1?"
indicating the "carried" digit. Jamal said it was the ten from 13.

The other children in the group seemed to be following the discussion
and were making comments. There was consensus in the group that this
method was a weird way. Adam said, "That's way harder. Why would
anyone do it that way?" The group agreed, and there were murmurs of
"I'm just not going to learn it," and "Me either."

This was a painful decision point for me. I had gone into the lesson
with fairly clear goals. I wanted the children in this group to think flexibly
and solve these problems several different ways, one of which should
be the conventional algorithm. I wanted them to know the algorithm for
third grade and beyond, although I did not want to place more value on
it than on the other methods. But the very fact that I was thinking they
should solve problems lots of different ways, one of which had to be "the
pink way," automatically placed much more value on this new, weird
method, one that did not come from the students. I now realized I had
conflicting goals between validating all the different methods of adding
and wanting to be sure that everyone learned the algorithm.

I ended up saying something like, it was wonderful how they had
ways of thinking that made sense to them, and that they were able to
stretch their brains to understand how someone else was thinking. I

added that I did want them to stretch their brains further and try to figure out this new method, partly because some adults and teachers would expect them to know it. Their response was interesting. They wondered why some teachers thought this was the "best" way, a translation they made, of course, despite my delicate phrasing. They decided that it was because this way is harder, and therefore "more math-y." Now that they were older and smarter, went their reasoning, they should do things a harder way. I often tell them that I give them hard work because it stretches them, and that they are able to do it; when work is just hard enough, they do their best learning.

Anyway, next I gave the children another word problem and told them I wanted them to solve it using at least two different methods. They attacked it with gusto. Most of them tried the pink way as one method. Many of the children used all the methods shown on the poster. What amazed me was that they could all make some sense of the pink way.

I am not saying that the whole group now knows and understands that algorithm, but during this math period they were all able to use it to add 49 and 39. They talked to each other and helped each other. Some children wrote the numbers side by side instead of in vertical columns and got confused. Others wrote the numbers vertically, but left out the line that separates the addends from the sum. Yet they all found a way into the procedure and how it works.

I remember despairing last year because the children had been pretty consistently perplexed by what I wanted of them during trading games and this adding process. They had been hard-working and conscientious children in general, but most of them did not understand how this algorithm relates to addition, or place value, or trading.

I think a very important difference this year was that by the time these ten children were exposed to the traditional algorithm, they had successfully constructed their own understandings of addition with regrouping. They were comfortable thinking of numbers in terms of tens and ones; this had meaning for them. Therefore their task was different. Now I was asking them to reconcile a new method with what they *already knew*. Last year, on the other hand, I had been wanting the class to construct an understanding of tens and ones, how numbers are made up, and how numbers combine, all at once—using one particular method that made no sense to them.

And what about the other twelve children in my class this year? I have many children whose grasp of tens and ones and of place value is

less developed than it is for the ten children I met with initially. Given
the same word problem, several of the remaining kids started at 38 and
counted on 25 by ones. Two made Unifix cube collections of 38 and 25
and counted the whole thing by ones. A couple of them successfully
added the tens and added the ones, but were frozen when faced with
13 ones. All these children can identify the tens place in a two-digit
number. They can say how many tens and how many ones there are.
They understand counting by tens at some level. But they do not use this
knowledge when adding two-digit numbers.

Heather was laboriously counting on by ones to solve a word problem
that involved adding 49 and 39. Someone near her suggested that she
"use tens and ones." Heather said, "Oh, yeah!" and added the tens. Then
she added the ones. Then she combined them. She did not seem confident
or comfortable, but she did it. I wonder, though, what she was thinking.
Her initial impulse—to count on—made sense to her, because that was
what the problem suggested to her. She would probably have been sure
that what she was doing represented the story in the problem, and that
her result was the right answer. It seemed as if her friend's suggestion
triggered her memory of a procedure, but I am not at all convinced that
she was sure the "tens and ones" procedure matched counting on or the
story problem in any way.

Many of my children are still working on constructing a system
of tens and ones. Until they do, the traditional algorithm will not make
sense to them.

C A S E   13

# Subtraction and invented algorithms

## Lynn

Every time we work on it, I think my appreciation for the complexities
of subtraction increases. My students have been solving word problems
involving two-digit addition and subtraction both with and without

regrouping. They have been working on explaining and recording their processes for solving the problems. Our work with addition has been interesting and satisfying, and, as I find every year, subtraction proves to be more problematic than addition for seven- and eight-year-olds.

One word problem involved pigeons in the park: First there were 39 of them, and then a dog came along and 17 flew away, the question being, How many pigeons remained? Children solved this problem in an even wider variety of ways than I anticipated. As they worked and described their thinking, and as they tried to understand one another's thinking, the issue of how to keep track of what was going on kept arising.

Many children counted back from 39 to solve the problem. When they did so, several of them had to pause along the way. Isabel counted on her fingers and at first didn't know when to stop. She seemed to lose sight of the 17 she was counting back to represent the departed birds, and therefore wasn't sure when she got to the remaining birds. She was, however, able to start over with a little more clarity and figure out how to use her strategy successfully.

Some children also counted up from 17 to 39. At least one child, Sabrina, then pronounced the answer to be 39, rather than 22. At least part of her confusion could result from not being able to hold in mind all at once both the original problem and the meaning of her numbers and procedures. When children count up to join two numbers, the last number they say is the answer; that's probably why Sabrina thought 39 was the answer.

Children who used more complex strategies also seemed to have trouble keeping in mind both the meaning of the numbers and the problem context. They also had trouble keeping track of numbers they had taken apart for their calculations. Fiona worked on a variation of the word problem that involved regrouping (of 37 pigeons, 19 flew away). She dropped the 7 from the 37 for the time being. She then subtracted 10 from 30. Then she subtracted 9 more. She puzzled for a while about what to do with the 7 now that she had to put it back somewhere. Should she subtract it or add it? I asked her one question: "Did those 7 pigeons leave or stay?" She said they stayed, and added the 7.

$37 - 19$

$30 - 10 = 20$    $20 - 9 = 11$    $11 + 7 = 18$

It was interesting to me that Fiona needed only that one question to clear up her confusion, and I think for the most part she subtracts this way and keeps it straight. While Fiona goes through the steps in her algorithm, she is able to keep track of when to add and when to subtract. The 7 gets subtracted (from 37) and then added again (at the end, to 11). The 9 from the 19 is, in a way, added to the 10 in 19, but it is subtracted, because Fiona needs to subtract all of the 19. The 7 is part of what is being subtracted from. The 9 is part of what is being subtracted. It is a complicated process and it is amazing to me that a second grader can make sense of it for herself. I had a student last year who struggled with this very issue for weeks and never figured it out.

Paul also takes numbers apart to subtract. To solve $39 - 17$, he takes the 17 apart in three steps:

$$39 - 10 = 29 \quad 29 - 4 = 25 \quad 25 - 3 = 22$$

Paul keeps track of the 17 while breaking it into familiar chunks. Many children wondered where he got the 10, 4, and 3 from. How did he know what to subtract? How did he know when he was done?

Interestingly, Paul himself had questions for Nathan about how Nathan knew which numbers to put together for his answer. Here is Nathan's process for $39 - 17$:

$$17 + 3 = 20$$
$$20 + 10 = 30$$
$$30 + 9 = 39$$
$$3 + 10 + 9 = 22$$

Nathan nearly always adds, even for a straightforward separating situation like birds flying away. After Nathan explained how he solved this problem, Paul said, "But how does he know what numbers to add up at the end?"

I thought a little bit about the conventional algorithm. A few children use it sometimes, ever since I gave word problems for homework. Clearly, a family member had shown it to them. If a child memorizes the procedure, there is no real "keeping track." They must learn the steps, but they do not need to keep track of what the 3 in 37 means or how much of the 19 they have subtracted so far. If they get confused or forget a step or go out of order, children using this procedure tend not to go back and make sense of the numbers or the problem, or try to keep track of what is going on. I am not sure if this is unique to this algorithm, or if it happens because they have learned a procedure with no meaning in it.

Building a System of Tens

Finally, an almost unrelated observation: This year for the first time I have never seen a single child "subtract up" in the ones column if the bottom number is greater than the top one. In other years, I have always had many children do this.

$$\begin{array}{r} 37 \\ -\ 19 \\ \hline 22 \end{array}$$  because $3 - 1 = 2$ and $9 - 7 = 2$

I am not sure what to make of this, but I hope it is because this year the children carry more of the meaning of the problem with them, which they do because they are allowed to construct their own ways of solving it.

C A S E  **14**

# Partitioning subtraction problems

Nadine

Today I worked with a group of eleven students who are still sorting out the complexities of subtraction. I posed this problem:

$$\begin{array}{r} 387 \\ -\ 149 \end{array}$$

TEACHER: There are different ways to solve this problem, but all of them start with taking the problem apart in some way. Why do we take the problem apart?

NATHAN: Well, it would be really hard to just do 387 minus 149 in one step. I don't think anyone could do that. So you have to find smaller problems to make it easier.

TEACHER: How would you take this problem apart to make it easier to solve?

# Nadine

JANET:      I'd just work with each column separately.

TEACHER:    So what would your parts be?

JANET:      300, 80, 7 and 100, 40, 9.

TEACHER:    I know when Janet solves the problem, she doesn't write the
            parts out separately, but I'm going to do that to help us see
            what's happening with this strategy.

I wrote on the board:

$$300 \quad\quad 80 \quad\quad 7$$
$$\underline{-100 \quad\quad 40 \quad\quad 9}$$

TEACHER:    Who has a different way of pulling the problem apart?

STEPHEN:    I'd keep the 387 together and only pull apart the 149. I'd do
            that just like Janet did: 100, 40, 9.

NAOMI:      I'd do 380, 7 and 140, 9.

JUANITA:    I'd do 380, 7 and 100, 49.

I wonder how Naomi and Juanita will deal with their 7 and 9 or 7 and
49, but decide to let the students decide which way of partitioning they
want to examine first. At this point, we have the following written down.

$$387$$
$$\underline{-149}$$

| Janet | 300 | 80 | 7 |
|---|---|---|---|
|  | $\underline{-100}$ | $\underline{40}$ | $\underline{9}$ |
| Stephen | 387 | | |
|  | 100 | 40 | 9 |
| Naomi | 380 | 7 | |
|  | 140 | 9 | |
| Juanita | 380 | 7 | |
|  | 100 | 49 | |

66                                              Building a System of Tens

# Nadine

GRADE 4, FEBRUARY

TEACHER: Which way of breaking the problem apart will help you solve it? Which way would make it easiest for you?

ALBERT: I'd use Stephen's way.

I recorded as Albert presented his steps.

$$387 - 100 = 287$$
$$287 - 40 = 247$$
$$247 - 9 = 238$$

At the last step, Albert paused as he thought through the answer to $247 - 9$.

TEACHER: Can someone else talk us through Stephen's way? I noticed that Albert's last step was the hardest. Is there a way to make it easier?

As Mary explained her strategy, I took the opportunity to record it in a different format.

$$
\begin{array}{r}
387 \\
-100 \\
\hline
287 \\
-\;40 \\
\hline
247 \\
-\;\;7 \\
\hline
240 \\
-\;\;2 \\
\hline
238
\end{array}
$$

NATHAN: Instead of subtracting 9, I'd subtract 10 and do $247 - 10 = 237$. Then I'd have to add 1.

TEACHER: I know you already know the right answer, so it's easy to see that you have to add 1, but I wonder if you can explain it another way. Why do you have to add 1 at the end?

NATHAN: Well, you can't just put 1 on the 9 and leave it like that. You have to do something with it at the end. This is subtraction so you have to add it at the end. If this was addition, you'd subtract it at the end.

Chapter 3

67

325
330
335
340
345
350
355

# Nadine

TEACHER: Can anyone else explain why Nathan has to add 1 at the end?

STEPHEN: He took away too much, so he has to put 1 back.

TEACHER: Does anyone want to explain how taking the problem apart in a different way will make the problem easier to solve?

HALLIE: I'd do it Janet's way.

As Hallie explained her strategy, I recorded it as follows:

$$
\begin{array}{rrr}
300 & 80 & 7 \\
-\,100 & 40 & 9 \\
\hline
200 & +\,40 & -\,2 = 240 - 2 = 238
\end{array}
$$

We talked briefly about where her −2 came from.

TEACHER: Hallie said she was going to do it Janet's way, but I see Janet shaking her head. Hallie's way certainly works, but it's not the way Janet had in mind.

JANET: I start with the ones. You can't take 9 from 7.

We paused to note that Hallie just did take 9 from 7, but Janet didn't want to get into negative numbers. She began her explanation again.

JANET: You can't take 9 from 7 without getting negatives, so I need to take 1 from the 8. No, I need to take 10 from the 80 and make it a 70. Then I give the 10 to the 7 and make it 17. Now I can subtract the 9.

$$
\begin{array}{rrr}
 & 70 & \\
 & \cancel{80} & {}^{1}7 \\
300 & & \\
-\,100 & 40 & 9 \\
\hline
200 & +\,30 & +\,8 = 238
\end{array}
$$

I noted to myself that, seeing the numbers written out in expanded notation, Janet corrected herself as she began to say that she took 1 from the 8. She knows she took 10 from 80.

Other students nodded their heads as they watched what Janet did. I know most of these students don't use the U.S. standard algorithm

Building a System of Tens

successfully, but many of them try it. I saw this as an opportunity to build    385
more foundation for understanding it and to raise questions about Janet's
method. I gave a new problem:

$$\begin{array}{r} 503 \\ -247 \\ \hline \end{array}$$

Students described how to break it apart using Janet's way:    390

$$\begin{array}{ccc} 500 & & 3 \\ -\,200 & 40 & 7 \\ \end{array}$$

HALLIE:    You can't do 3 minus 7 if you're doing it Janet's way. So you
need to get 10 more to put with the 3. There aren't any tens
numbers. So you have to start by making the 500 a 400.    395

TEACHER:    What will you do with the 100 Hallie took out of the 500?

There were lots of confused looks. I let the students think and then asked
again. Responses included:

You could make it 100 ones.
You could make it 50.    400
You could make it 60.

In response to the latter suggestions, I asked, "And just throw away the
rest? Is that equal to Hallie's 100?" Then I pushed students to tell me how
to get what we need to subtract the 7.

NAOMI:    You could put 90 and then give the other 10 to the 3 and    405
make it 13.

With Naomi's suggestion, we finish the problem.

$$\begin{array}{ccc} 400 & 90 & \\ \cancel{500} & & {}^{1}3 \\ -\,200 & 40 & 7 \\ \hline 200 & +\,50 & +\,6 = 256 \\ \end{array}$$

410

Now the session was over. Stephen asked, "Why did we use only two
of the ways on the chart instead of all four?"

I answered, "Because we're out of time. Maybe we can return to these
next time."

# Nadine

I liked working with this group separately. I sense that with the slower pacing and focused work, many of them were figuring things out for themselves as we went along. In spite of my use of wait time in whole-class discussions, things can still move too quickly and too many ideas get introduced for some of these students to keep up. They are also more willing to offer their own ideas in this group.

In this session, we never did explore Naomi's and Juanita's ideas for how to break apart the problem. Maybe we will return to them as Stephen wants us to. Trying out ideas that don't work easily, or don't work easily for a variety of problems, is important in helping students evaluate strategies.

415

420

425

70                                                    Building a System of Tens

# CHAPTER
# 4

# Multiplication of multidigit numbers

| | | |
|---|---|---|
| **C A S E  1 5** | 27 × 4, or dogs looking for scraps | *Eleanor, Grades 3 and 4, December* |
| **C A S E  1 6** | From concept to computation | *Susannah, Grade 3, April* |
| **C A S E  1 7** | Does it fit? | *Al, Grade 7, September* |
| **C A S E  1 8** | Connecting images of multiplication to algebra | *Jayson, Grade 9, September* |

The casebook began with a look at students' various methods for adding and subtracting multidigit numbers. This led to questions about how students come to understand the structure of multidigit numbers and how they can apply that understanding when they add and subtract. Now we ask similar questions about multiplication: How can large numbers be decomposed and recombined in order to multiply them? What ideas about place value are significant and need to be tracked as students multiply?

To prepare yourself for the reasoning that students use in this chapter's cases, you might first try using various representations of multiplication yourself. For example, how could you draw a diagram, or arrange manipulatives, to

71

represent 16 × 18? Do such representations suggest ways in which you might decompose the numbers to make the multiplication more manageable?

As you read the cases, take notes on the students' methods and consider the following questions:

■ What ideas about multiplication come into play as the students work on multiplying numbers that have been decomposed?

■ What errors arise and how do the students sort them out?

■ How do the representations used by Jayson's ninth graders help them keep track of the components of the multiplication problems?

Although the students in the cases are in third to ninth grade, teachers of younger children can consider the following:

■ What mathematical ideas developed in the earlier grades support this work in multiplication?

■ What do my students already understand about multiplication?

■ How can I help my students extend their ideas and build concepts that will support this later work?

C A S E    15

# 27 × 4, or dogs looking for scraps

## *Eleanor*

GRADES 3 AND 4, DECEMBER

While working on multiplication with the nine- and ten-year-olds I teach, I am trying to discover what signs and landmarks will tell me when they are ready to move beyond multiplication. That is, when do these children understand multiplication well enough, and just how do nine- and ten-year-olds understand it?

As part of their multiplication work, I have asked kids to work with arrays, to play games with them, to study them. We have had discussions

about the operations and how to use them flexibly—choosing to use
addition and multiplication in the same problem, depending on the
numbers. We have talked about multiplying two-digit numbers and                    10
where addition and subtraction come into play. We have used base ten
blocks and graph paper. The children have written story problems based
on math sentences I gave them, and they have responded with math
sentences based on story problems I have written.

Recently I gave eight children a page, for homework, that asks them                15
to solve $27 \times 4$ in two different ways. In their written work, I found more
clues about what they are understanding now.

Mark wrote:

First way: I added all the 20s which got to 80 and then I added four
sevens and got 108.
                                                                                   20
Second way: I added the 20s but then I realized a shorter way than
adding. I just did $4 \times 7$ which is 28 so $80 + 20 = 100$ plus 8 more is 108.

Joel wrote:

First way: Well, $2 \times 27 = 54$, so $54 + 54 = 108$.

Second way: First I added up all of the 20s and got 80 and then I added              25
up all the sevens and got 28 and then I added 80 to 28 and got 108. [*Joel
also added little notes that* $4 \times 20 = 80$, *and* $4 \times 7 = 28$, *and* $80 + 28 = 108$.]

Stephan wrote:

First way: I used my head only. I added 27 and 27 and I got 54, then I
added 54 and 54 and I got the answer 108. I added 27 and 27 because           30
I knew it was half of $4 \times 27$, so I put the two halves together and I
got 108.

Second way: I knew that 27 was 20 plus 7 so I multiplied $4 \times 20$ and I
got 80. Then I added $4 \times 7$ (and I got 28) to 80 and I got 108.

Jen wrote:                                                                           35

First way: $2 \times 27 = 54$     $2 + 2 = 4$     $4 \times 27 = 108$
$54 + 54 = 108$
I found out that $2 \times 27 = 54$ and then I added $54 + 54$.

Second way: $20 \times 4 = 80$     $7 \times 4 = 28$
I did $80 + 28$.                                                                      40
$20 \times 4$ and $7 \times 4$ and then added them together.

Mika used similar strategies; she also pointed out that $4 \times 25 = 100$ and $2 \times 4 = 8$, so $100 + 8 = 108$.

The rest of the children's responses were very similar to these; all seem reasonable and thoughtful ways of going about multiplying in this instance. Looking overall at the integration of fact and facility, I see that the children are well on their way to understanding multiplication.

I have watched with particular pleasure the development of Jen's thinking. Ten days ago I had given this same group a story problem about 14 people buying 16 things each. In her math log, Jen interpreted this problem as $14 \times 16$. She also wrote:

$$2 = 28 \quad 3 = 42 \quad 6 = 84 \quad 7 = 103 \quad 14 = 206 \quad 16 = 234$$

Jen's arithmetic is off, but her strategy is a good one, anyway. This week I gave the group a story problem Mark made up:

> **?** One night 63 dogs were looking for scraps in people's garbage cans. Each dog got 12 scraps and then went home to bed. How many scraps did they get all together?

Jen went up to the board within minutes and wrote:

$$2 \times 63 = 126$$
$$4 \times 63 = 252$$
$$8 \times 63 = 504$$
$$12 \times 63 = 756$$

Jen shows great progress in the past two weeks; in the "dog scraps" problem, she is now using notation for multiplication in a way that states her ideas more powerfully; the notation is becoming a standard form for her. By adding the last two steps ($4 \times 63$ and $8 \times 63$) together to find $12 \times 63$, Jen indicates a solid grasp of the idea that she can partition and regroup the 12.

Although there were other ideas involved, Jen saw in the "dog scraps" question $8 + 4 = 12$ and used that. Yet in the "people buying things" problem, her approach was less direct. I wonder if the presence of such new material and so many ideas didn't give her too much to juggle. Had she found what 8 fourteens were, she might have simply doubled that and gotten her answer. Jen is a kid who often uses doubles as a working strategy; now that she has had some experience with multiplying, I think she might see that she could effectively use doubling in the "buying things" problem. I am fascinated by her work anyway, as I think that she is uniquely self-taught. I wonder what questions or problems I could pose for her to push her thinking.

So, back to the original question: When can I move beyond my concentration in this area of math? Before moving on, I would like to see that each child is as solid in her or his thinking as Jen. What do I see in her work that satisfies me her thinking is solid? There is a sturdiness to her understanding of the "dog scraps" problem that is evident in her direct steps, her direct notation, and her answer. I am satisfied that I can give Jen any multiplication problem now, and she will have a way of thinking about the problem—her own algorithm with which to start. I am not yet convinced that this is the case with the rest of the children in the group, so we will do more. I would like to step up the quality of the story problems I have been giving them, too. I feel as if the ones I have been offering are just standard number problems with a coating of words.

C A S E   16

# From concept to computation

## *Susannah*

It's that time of the year again when my third graders attempt (at my initiation) to transfer their knowledge of multiplication from concept to computation. Of course, we have been applying the ideas of multiplication all year, but now comes the challenge—for the students and for me to devise a multidigit multiplication procedure that is both meaningful and useful.

This year, I determined, my instruction would be different. I borrowed an idea from Marilyn Burns (1987), who writes in *A Collection of Math Lessons*, "Before resorting to paper and pencil computation, I think it is important to deal with multiplication mentally" (p. 33). Some of the examples she suggested seemed hard for my students to do mentally

# Susannah

("How many legs on 36 dogs?"), but after translating her ideas into problems relevant to my classroom, I presented the following warm-up-and-stretch-your-brain activity.

 We need 4 dozen eggs for Easter and Passover celebrations. How many must we buy?

Some children used the tried-and-true method of adding, with quick and accurate results.

KANEISHA:   I just doubled 12 to get 24 and then added 24 and 24 because that's four times, so 48.

Others were able to see the usefulness of breaking apart the numbers when I presented a problem with larger numbers.

 There were 64 teams at the beginning of the NCAA basketball tournament. With 5 players starting on each team, how many starting players were in the tournament?

"Wow, that's hard," proclaimed Debra loudly, and a chorus of protesters joined her. Undaunted, Laurel presented her thinking.

LAUREL:   That would be $64 \times 5$. I use one 10 because I know $5 \times 10 = 50$. Then you do that six times. [*She counted by fives, not using her fingers, but moving her lips and nodding her head for each group of five.*] That's 30, I mean 300. Then you add 4 five times, which is 25, no 20. I added it all together and got 320.

Chris, usually reticent and lacking in confidence, volunteered his thinking in a quiet, unassuming voice.

CHRIS:   $64$ means $60 + 4$. [*Silently I rejoiced that all our practice partitioning numbers was not forgotten.*] So I did 60 five times, for 300. Then $4 \times 5$ is 20, so the answer is 320.

Chris returned to his seat in a way I can only describe as cocky. I was certainly impressed.

Jack, our resident goof-off but intuitive math thinker, explained his strategy next.

JACK: I split the 64 into four parts—20, 20, and 20. [*Four parts, I wondered? But I waited without interrupting.*] I did each one separately. | 135

$20 \times 5 = 100$
$20 \times 5 = 100$
$20 \times 5 = 100$ | 140

Then the last part, $4 \times 5$, is 20. All together, 320.

These were the ideas and strategies I'd tried so hard to explain and instill in my students last year: breaking up numbers into useful parts, recognizing which numbers are being multiplied and by how much, finding a way to multiply that makes sense. Posing the right questions | 145
and relying on the children to use what they'd been practicing all year proved to be the solution to teaching multiplication. Of course, not everyone had moved beyond adding or understood what their classmates were doing. But they were listening and would begin to develop new strategies as we continued to multiply. | 150

The warm-up part of the math period was finished, and I was just about to hand out colored tiles for building arrays, when another multiplication opportunity presented itself.

TEACHER: We have 18 kids here today, and each one needs 12 tiles for the next activity. How can we figure out the number of tiles | 155
to give out?

A second later I realized this problem was a leap from the ones we'd just done, but it was "real life," so I let the question stand. I was surprised that no one suggested using a calculator, their usual response to big numbers. But who needs a calculator when you have Josh! | 160

JOSH: That would be $18 \times 12$, and I know $10 \times 10$ is 100 and $8 \times 2$ is 16, so if you add them together it would be $100 + 16 = 116$.

Everyone seemed satisfied with Josh's answer, whether out of agreement or lack of interest I wasn't sure. After all, the process | 165
mimicked what they'd just been doing. I was thinking about what to say that would help them see the error of their ways, when David's voice broke the quiet.

## susannah

GRADE 4, APRIL

DAVID:    That's wrong.

TEACHER:  What do you mean, David?

DAVID:    I did 18 × 10 and got 180, but I thought at first I was wrong,
so I double checked. I noticed that Josh didn't do 8 × 10,
so my answer was right. [*David is very knowledgeable about
the workings of our number system, but leaves gaps in his verbal
explanations. His mind races, and neither his mouth nor our
brains can keep up.*] I didn't do the 2 yet, so I do 18 × 2. Then
you add it up—180 + 36.

"Wow," I thought. I was amazed at his understanding, but realized
that the rest of the class looked dazed. Luckily, there will be more
chances for David and Josh and others to show what they know about
multiplication. I'll leave them to it and go out to lunch.

CASE 17

# Does it fit?

GRADE 7, SEPTEMBER

In our junior high school, at the beginning of the school year, we
give a placement test to determine whether the incoming seventh
graders will be placed in seventh-, eighth-, or ninth-grade math class.
For kids close to the cut-off score for any grade, I do a one-on-one
interview to recommend a placement. Toward the end of one such
interview, I asked Abbey some questions about decimal numbers,
specifically multiplication of decimal numbers. We both ended up
learning something new: Abbey developed a new understanding of the
steps of the U.S. standard algorithm for multiplying whole numbers; I
learned something about students' ability to reclaim their expectation to
make sense of mathematics.

## Making sense of an algorithm

I start by writing down these problems for Abbey to work out:

$$0 \times 3.4 =$$
$$1 \times 3.4 =$$
$$2 \times 3.4 =$$
$$3 \times 3.4 =$$

She proceeds without hesitation, giving responses of 0, 3.4, 6.8, and 10.2. I ask her how she did these, and she says she just kept adding 3.4 to the previous result. I then ask her where $1.2 \times 3.4$ would fit, and she quickly decides that it would be somewhere between 3.4 and 6.8, or between $1 \times 3.4$ and $2 \times 3.4$.

Asked to actually compute $1.2 \times 3.4$, Abbey works for a while and comes up with this:

$$12 \times 34 = 84$$
$$1.2 \times 3.4 = .84$$

She shows how the second line followed from the first line by moving the decimal point in the answer left by two places, one place for the 1.2, and another place for the 3.4.

I ask, "Where does your answer fit compared to how you thought it would fit?" Abbey decides that her answer must be wrong, because .84 is smaller than 3.4, and that can't be right. Seeming a little flustered, she quickly adds a 3 in front of the .84, resulting in 3.84, and says that this must be the real answer. I'm surprised, and my surprise shows as I ask her where she gets that 3 from. She crosses it out without saying anything. I assure her there is no hurry, suggesting that she slow down and take her time, and see if she can reconcile her result with where she thought it should fit. She checks her work on $12 \times 34$, doing it a second time:

$$
\begin{array}{r}
12 \\
\times\ 34 \\
\hline
48 \\
+\ 36 \\
\hline
84 \\
\end{array}
$$

I see her problem, but I'm not sure how to get Abbey to see it for herself. I ask her if she thinks $34 \times 12$ should give the same answer. She says yes. She then does the arithmetic for $34 \times 12$:

```
     34
   ×  12
     68
   + 34
    102
```

230

Abbey is now clear that her problem lies in her multiplication, but she seems unsure how to fix it. She doesn't trust her 102 answer, either. I ask her if she has another way of doing the multiplication that would allow her to be sure of her answer. She says something about adding, so I write twelve 34s as a vertical addition problem, asking her if this is what she had in mind (Figure 4.1, left).

235

Abbey counts the 34s, finds 12, and offers that this is 34, twelve times, and should give the same answer as 34 × 12.

Asked to work out this version of the multiplication, Abbey seems energized and confident, a real shift from the hesitation she has been showing so far. This seems to be a representation she can get her hands around. She starts with the unit column, counting down to ten, saying "ten fours, that's 40, and two more, for 48." She is approaching this addition problem by multiplying! She writes down the 8 and carries the 4 (Figure 4.1, center). Then she approaches the threes from the bottom, counting up ten rows and saying "ten threes, that's 30, and two more threes and a four, for 40" (Figure 4.1, right).

240

245

| | | 4 | | 4 |
|---|---|---|---|---|
| | 34 | 34 | | 34 |
| | 34 | 34 | | 34 |
| | 34 | 34 | | 34 |
| | 34 | 34 | | 34 |
| | 34 | 34 | | 34 |
| | 34 | 34 | | 34 |
| | 34 | 34 | | 34 |
| | 34 | 34 | | 34 |
| | 34 | 34 | | 34 |
| | 34 | 34 | | 34 |
| | 34 | 34 | | 34 |
| + | 34 | + 34 | | + 34 |
| | | 8 | | 408 |

**Figure 4.1**  Abbey's work to understand 34 × 12.

Abbey looks at me expectantly. Since this is a third answer for 12 × 34, different from both her previous answers, I ask how she can be confident of this one. What she does surprises me completely. She remembers the original problem! "Oh, I just put the decimal point in, and now 4.08 does fall between the 3.4 and the 6.8." She then goes straight to her version of 34 × 12 and fixes it without prompting:

```
    34                    34
  × 12                  × 12
    68      fixed to      68
  + 34                   340
   102                   408
```

I ask her what she discovered, and she responds that she was treating the 1 in 12 like a one instead of like a ten.

## Where does this fit?

After many years of seeing kids apply half-remembered standard algorithms in ways that clearly don't make sense to them, I continue to be shocked every time this behavior shows up. I wonder for how many kids math doesn't make sense, and I wonder how many kids have completely given up on expecting math to make sense. Yet even kids who appear to have given that up seem to be able to invent whole sections of math on the fly when looking at a representation that makes sense to them.

For Abbey, seeing twelve 34s in a column to be added up was as concrete a representation as she needed to invent her own version of multiplication, simply as a time-saving approach to avoid doing a whole lot of adding. She even showed she was able to use her new insight to reconstruct the U.S. standard algorithm from her faulty memory of it. I am left wondering if this is a natural outcome of somebody reclaiming the insistence that math make sense.

I am also becoming aware of my bias toward probing errors and not probing correct answers. It was obvious that Abbey misapplied the multiplication algorithm, doing it from memory without making sense. Yet the way she moved the decimal points over might similarly have been done from memory, without any logic. But because she moved the decimal points correctly, I did not probe how she made sense out of that action.

Finally, I am struck by the power of having bounds for your answer before you compute it in detail. Abbey's confidence in 408 and her lack of confidence in 84 and 102 might have been very different without the previously established expectation that 1.2 × 3.4 fit between 3.4 and 6.8.

285

CASE 18

# Connecting images of multiplication to algebra

## Jayson

GRADE 9, SEPTEMBER

Charlene and I graduated from college at the same time, and over the years we have continued to learn together about the mathematical thinking of our students. Although I am currently working as a student-teacher supervisor in secondary mathematics for a local university, I still take the opportunity to drop in on Charlene's middle school math classes from time to time to see what the students are working on.

290

### Part 1: Strategies for multiplying 23 × 84

One of the issues Charlene and I explore is how middle school mathematics students connect their strategies and models for multiplying numbers to their thinking about multiplying algebraic expressions. As I observe algebra classes, I have a growing concern that the way students add, subtract, multiply, and divide algebraic expressions has little connection to their images of these operations from earlier work with arithmetic.

295

Charlene's algebra students have been using area models to multiply algebraic expressions. Area models are similar to open arrays, except the sides are of undetermined length, denoted by a variable, such as $x$, or an expression, such as $x + 3$. To draw these diagrams, students usually begin with an $x$-by-$x$ square and then extend the sides to create the

300

$(x + 2)$ by $(x + 3)$ rectangle. A product of algebraic expressions such as $(x + 2)(x + 3)$ can be recorded as the sum of the area of smaller rectangles. For example, the diagram below shows a rectangle whose area can be described as the product of the lengths of the sides, $(x + 2)(x + 3)$, or as the sum of the area of smaller rectangles, $x^2 + 3x + 2x + 6$.

305

|     | $x$   | 3   |
|-----|-------|-----|
| $x$ | $x^2$ | $3x$ |
| 2   | $2x$  | 6   |

$(x + 2)(x + 3) = x^2 + 3x + 2x + 6$

After working on these algebraic models for awhile, including some examples such as $(x - 2)(x + 3)$ where one side of the rectangle is decreased by an amount, Charlene asked students to think about strategies they might use to multiply $23 \times 84$. Students shared the following methods.

310

Richard made a first attempt (shown at left). Then, when asked by a classmate where he got the 24, he rewrote his work (as seen at right), changing both the 24 and the 160.

315

```
    23              23
  × 84            × 84
    12              12
    80              80
    24             240
   160            1600
   276            1932
```

Mark presented his approach this way:

```
   23          10          10          3
 × 84        × 84        × 84        × 84
             840         840         252
 _____       _____

                  1680     +     252   =   1932
```

## Jayson

GRADE 9, SEPTEMBER

Emily volunteered, "I learned it different. Can I do it a different way?"
She wrote:

$$
\begin{array}{r}
^2 \\
^1 \\
23 \\
\times\ 84 \\
\hline
92 \\
184X \\
\hline
1932
\end{array}
$$

Caden presented this method:

$$
\begin{array}{r}
20 \\
\times\ 84 \\
\hline
0 \\
80 \\
0 \\
1600 \\
\hline
1680
\end{array}
\qquad
\begin{array}{r}
3 \\
\times\ 84 \\
\hline
12 \\
240 \\
\hline
252
\end{array}
\qquad
\begin{array}{r}
252 \\
1680 \\
\hline
1932
\end{array}
$$

Karl simply started out this way:

```
//////////////////////
//////////////////////
//////////////////////
```

Karl said he was going to make 84 rows of 23 tally marks and count
them up one at a time. Students suggested that maybe there would be
ways to group the tally marks to make them easier to count. However,
no one suggested a particular way to do this and the class moved on to
another strategy.

Jackson explained, "I found the area of a rectangle whose area is
23 × 84, but I broke it up into more manageable blocks." He drew
an area model:

|      | 80   | 4  |
|------|------|----|
| 20   | 1600 | 80 |
| 3    | 240  | 12 |

$$1600 + 240 + 80 + 12 = 1932$$

84                                                  Building a System of Tens

# Jayson

GRADE 9, SEPTEMBER

Then Richard spoke up again with a second strategy. "Sometimes you can do a related problem. Like if you were going to find 72 × 98, you know the answer is way close to 7,200. Then you just need to subtract off 2 × 98 = 196." Some students said they thought he should subtract 2 × 72 = 144. After thinking for a moment, Richard agreed. "Oh, yeah. I need to subtract two groups of 72."

## Part 2: Using 10 × 20 as the first step for 13 × 24 or 13 × 18

At this point Charlene and I were curious about how students might connect their work with multiplying algebraic expressions to these multiplication problems with numbers, so I proposed that Charlene have her students work on the following two problems:

Answer the following questions without using calculators or the standard multiplication algorithm.

1. John knows that 10 × 20 = 200. He wants to use this fact to find the product 13 × 24. John thinks he needs to add 12 to 200 to get the answer, since 13 is 3 more than 10, and 24 is 4 more than 20, and 3 × 4 = 12. What do you think?

   (A) John is right. He will get the correct answer by adding 12 more to 200.

   (B) John is wrong. To get the correct answer he needs to add _____ to 200 because . . .

2. Now John needs to know the product 13 × 18, and again he wants to get the answer by adding or subtracting something from the product 10 × 20 = 200. Explain how to figure out how much he should add or subtract to get the correct answer.

Some students, like Dana, felt that John's work on question 1 was correct. He explained his thinking.

DANA: Well, this equation would look like this. First you split the two numbers. [*On his paper, Dana showed 13 being split into 10 and 3, and 24 into 20 and 4.*] You'd plug these numbers into this equation: (10 × 20) + (3 × 4). Then you'd simplify it. 10 × 20 = 200 and 3 × 4 = 12. So John is correct because he is using the same numbers.

Other students carried out the actual multiplication to see how much larger than 200 the answer would be. If they used the conventional multiplication algorithm, the 200 and the 12 were not as apparent as they were for those who paid attention to the partial products, such as in this example from Kristi:

365

*When you put the equation in this form*

    13
    24
    ──

    12 (4·3)
    40 (4·10)
    60 (20·30)     *he forgot about*
    200 (20·10)    *these two*

I wondered if Emily was thinking about groups of objects when she wrote the following to explain the missing pieces:

370

13 is 3 more than 10, so to make up for the additional 3, you do 3 × 20 = 60. 24 is 4 more than 20, so to make up for the extra 4 you do 4 × 10 = 40. But then you also need to make up for the missing 3 [from 13], so you do 4 × 3 = 12. Then you add up all the extra to get 112. Add 112 to 200 to get the answer for 13 × 24 which is 312.

375

Only three students, Richard, Caden, and Jackson, used an area model to think about the partial products in the multiplication. Jackson included an explanation with his drawing:

380

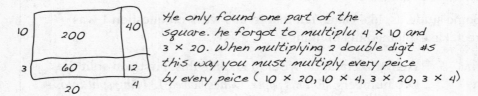

*He only found one part of the square. he forgot to multiply 4 × 10 and 3 × 20. When multiplying 2 double digit #s this way you must multiply every peice by every peice ( 10 × 20, 10 × 4, 3 × 20, 3 × 4)*

Building a System of Tens

# Jayson

GRADE 9, SEPTEMBER

For question 2, most students ignored the statement that John wanted to start with $10 \times 20 = 200$ and modify that product in some way to get the answer for $13 \times 18$. Some used the U.S. standard multiplication algorithm to get 234, and then reported that John would need to add 34 to 200 to get the correct answer. The 200 doesn't show up in the standard algorithm, nor did it show up in Richard's area model for this problem:

385

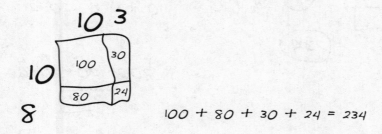

$$100 + 80 + 30 + 24 = 234$$

Caden's "area model" wasn't really about area since he extended one side of his rectangle to show the –2, but it did give him a way to keep track of what he needed to add and subtract from 200:

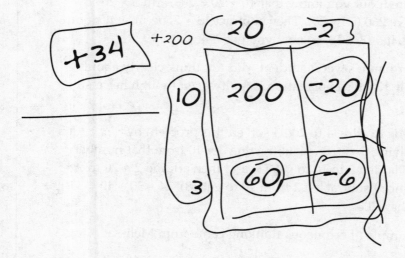

Only Jackson's area model matched the context of the situation, starting with a 10-by-20 rectangle, increasing the shorter side by 3, and

390

decreasing the longer side by 2. Jackson also connected this drawing to the distributive property (which he refers to as FOIL).

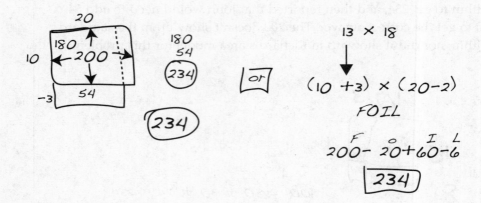

Other students were able to think about modifying the product $10 \times 20 = 200$ without using an area model. Although no one discussed the problem in terms of groups of objects, there seemed to be some underlying sense of keeping track of amounts, as in this explanation from Heather:

> To figure it out you know that $10 \cdot 20 = 200$, add $3 \cdot 20$ so you have 260 ($13 \cdot 20$). Then subtract $13 \cdot 2$, because it's not $13 \cdot 20$, it's $13 \cdot 18$, so now you get 234.

On the other hand, several students did not think clearly about question 2 at all. Kristi's explanation is faulty even though her result is correct:

> He needs to add 34 to 200. I solved this problem by multiplying $3 \cdot 8$, then subtracting $3 \cdot 10$ from that number (since I added 3 to 10 to get 13) and then adding $2 \cdot 20$ to that (since I subtracted 2 from 20 to get 18). $24 - 30 + 40 = 34$ more than 200.

Another example of erroneous thinking came from Melissa:

> Now John needs to know $13 \times 18$ and he wants to use his same method: get the answer by adding or subtracting

some number to the product of 10 × 20. First comes
8 × 3, then 8 × 10, then 10 × 3, then 10 × 10. That's the
ORDINARY way to do it. But since we're rounding 18 to 20,
things change. THIS way, 13 × 18 is the same as 13 × 20 –
13 × 3 [*sic*]. But we also have to round 13 to 10. THAT way,
13 × 18 is the same as 13 × 20 – 13 × 3 + 2 × 18. You have to
multiply 18 by 2 because 18 is 2 away from 20. You have to
multiply 13 by 3 because 13 is 3 away from 10. Let's restate
our equation:  10 × 20 – 13 × 3 + 2 × 18 = 13 × 18. That's
200 – 39 + 36 = 197 = 13 × 18."

As I have reviewed the students' work on these two questions, I've
wondered why only a few of them saw the area model or the distributive
property as a reasonable way to think through these two situations.
After all, they have been using the distributive property in multiplying
algebraic expressions since their previous year in algebra (although it has
been proceduralized for them as FOIL: multiply First, Outer, Inner, and
Last terms, and then add the results), and in Charlene's class they have
been using area models to develop a conceptual understanding of
multiplying algebraic expressions. So why are these ideas not more
accessible to students when they think about multiplying numbers?
Do many of them see any connection between the multiplication they
encountered in arithmetic and the multiplication they are doing in
algebra? Would seeing such a connection help?

## Part 3: Computational flexibility translates to algebraic flexibility

There is a footnote to these observations. Initially in this unit, the only
strategy Charlene's students used to multiply algebraic expressions was
the FOIL method, but when asked to multiply $(x + 2)(3x + 5)$ after this
discussion, the following methods were noted by a pre-service college
student who was observing the class that day:

415

420

425

430

435

440

## Jayson

GRADE 9, SEPTEMBER

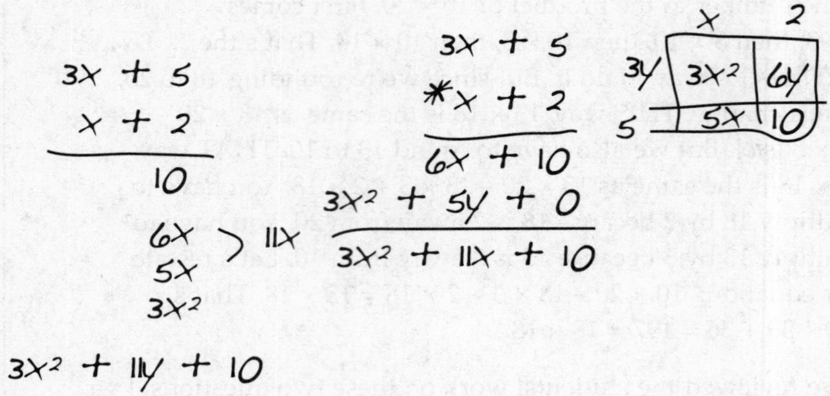

$$3x + 5$$
$$\underline{\phantom{3}x + 2}$$
$$10$$
$$6x \enspace \big\rangle \enspace 11x$$
$$5x$$
$$3x^2$$

$$3x^2 + 11x + 10$$

$$3x + 5$$
$$\underline{*x + 2}$$
$$6x + 10$$
$$\underline{3x^2 + 5y + 0}$$
$$3x^2 + 11x + 10$$

Maybe the students are making some connections between their images of multiplication and their methods for multiplying algebraic expressions after all.

Building a System of Tens

# CHAPTER

# 5

# Division with multidigit numbers

| CASE 19 | Let me count the tens | Susie, Grade 6, March |
| --- | --- | --- |
| CASE 20 | Discussing division | Eleanor, Grades 3 and 4, October |
| CASE 21 | Sharing jelly beans | Janie, Grade 4, April |
| CASE 22 | Making sense of division | Maeve, Grade 4, March |

In chapter 5, we look at division in terms of mathematical questions similar to those addressed elsewhere in this casebook. As you read the following cases, take notes on these questions:

■ How is dividing by 10 related to place value?

■ How can large numbers be decomposed and recombined in order to divide?

■ In what ways do the strategies for decomposing numbers work or not work for division?

Although the students in the cases are in third to sixth grade, teachers of younger children can consider the following:

- What mathematical ideas developed in the earlier grades support this work in division?

- What do my students already understand about division?

- How can I help my students extend their ideas and build concepts that will support this later work?

C A S E   19

# Let me count the tens

## Susie

GRADE 6, MARCH

I am a math coach, and earlier in the year I visited a sixth-grade class to explore some ideas related to place value. I asked the students to read a set of large numbers that were typed on cards, and then asked them to find the number of thousands in 473,812 (as described in case 11). The students really struggled. Why was this a difficult task? As I watched their struggles, I wondered if working with hundreds or tens would be as difficult as working with thousands. After a few months, I decided to revisit the class and pursue this idea. At the beginning of the lesson, I wrote the number 4,763 on the board.

TEACHER:     How many tens are in 4,763?

GABRIELLA:   What do you mean? Like, just in the tens place or in the whole number?

TEACHER:     How many tens are in the whole number?

GABRIELLA:   I think 530.

TEACHER:     How did you get that answer?

Building a System of Tens

# Susie

GABRIELLA: There is 4,000, so I divided by 10, and it's 400. Then
I did 700 divided by 10 and I got 70. Then I added those
two and I got 470. Then there are 60 left, and I divided 60
by 10 and I got 60, and I added them together. But there are
really only 6, so it would be 476.

JAMES: No, it's 476.3.

TEACHER: James, how did you get the 3 tenths?

JAMES: Because 10 ones make a ten, so 3 tens will be .3. Three will be
3 tenths and we got an entire tenth, so it would be a fraction
of a tenth.

TEACHER: Do you mean tenths or tens?

JAMES: Basically I divided the whole number by a 10 and I got 476.3.
When we're dividing by a 10, we just move the decimal
point over, because when you divide by 10 that's all you
have to do.

TEACHER: How does "moving the decimal point over" work?

JAMES: It's like working in the metric system. Like, you have 10
centimeters and then like you divide it, and you get like a
kilometer. I don't really know what I'm saying.

RACHEL: In the ones place, the number is never going to be higher
than 10 because it would have to go to the tens place, so
moving the decimal over will work.

TEACHER: But there isn't a decimal in 4,763.

ALLI: There's always a decimal after everything.

JAMES: Once you divide by 10, the decimal will just come over just
because that's what happens on the calculator.

I listened carefully to see what the students understood about moving
the decimal over. So far, I knew that James had used the calculator to get
his answer, which told me he knew *how* to get the answer, but did James
understand *why* 476.3 was a correct response?

TEACHER: Why does that work?

ALLI:          It's kind of like timesing, when you add a zero. Like when you times 6 by 10 and get 60, you just move the number over and add a zero.

TEACHER:       You said two things that I want to ask about. First, how is dividing like multiplying? Second, what do you mean about moving the number over?

ALLI:          When you divide by 10, it's like multiplying.

TEACHER:       Sadie, can you explain what Alli is saying?

SADIE:         Here, let me show you.

Sadie wrote the problem on the board. Using the traditional algorithm for division, she modeled how to solve the problem, but did not connect it to multiplication.

$$
\begin{array}{r}
476.3\phantom{0} \\
10\overline{)4763.0} \\
\underline{40\phantom{00.0}} \\
76\phantom{0.0} \\
\underline{70\phantom{0.0}} \\
63\phantom{.0} \\
\underline{60\phantom{.0}} \\
30 \\
\underline{30} \\
\end{array}
$$

TEACHER:       Mike, can you explain what Sadie is doing?

MIKE:          She's dividing 4,763 by 10.

SADIE:         [*not waiting for me to question Mike about why she chose to divide*] Well, you just divide like I did, and you can have a remainder, and you can make it into a fraction or you can make it into a decimal, but I just made it a decimal just because…

JAMES:         OK, when she said that timesing and dividing by 10 are the same, when you times by 10, you will always get a zero after it.

TEACHER:       Why?

Building a System of Tens

JAMES: 'Cause um…

ALLI: 'Cause since you're making everything like 10 times bigger, and so it's like going to move up a spot from the ones place to the tens place and from the tens place to the hundreds place. You're making everything bigger, you're making everything 10 times bigger.

JAMES: When you divide, it's like your decimal still stays in the same spot.

TEACHER: [*sensing that the students are getting frustrated*] I can tell that you know a lot about this, but you haven't explained why this works. Does the decimal move or does the decimal stay in the same place? Alli says the number "moves up a spot." What happens to the number when we multiply or divide?

ALLI: You do it because there's this in the tens spot [*pointing to the 6*], you're not going to have this [*pointing to the 3*] because it's not a whole ten. This works, because 10 will go into it evenly, will go into the 60 evenly, but not the 3.

SADIE: The 3 is not a whole number, so you can't use it.

JAMES: You mean it's not a whole ten. It has to be bigger than 10, or there's no way it will work.

TEACHER: We talked about how many tens there are in 4,763; how many hundreds are in that number?

RACHEL: There are 47.

TEACHER: Are there really 47 hundreds in 4,763? Is 4,700 the same as 47 hundreds?

GABRIELLA: Well, no…

TEACHER: Gabriella, does the rule of changing spots work for hundreds?

GABRIELLA: It probably works for all numbers, but I'm not sure there are 47 hundreds in 4,700.

# susie

I began to wonder about including tenths and hundredths in our next discussion.

**TEACHER:** Earlier in our discussion, when I asked how many tens are in 4,763, James gave me an answer of 476.3. I've been wondering about the 3 tenths. James, can you explain why you said there were 3 tenths in this answer?

**JAMES:** I don't think I said it right. There isn't a whole 10 in the ones place. There is just 3, so we have 3, but we're missing 7 to make it a ten. So it's like a fraction of three tenths, so it's point 3.

**TEACHER:** Is it possible to find the number of tenths in 4,763?

**GABRIELLA:** Yeah, if you use the calculator.

**ALLI:** It would work if you moved the decimal. I think it would be 47,630 or 476,300 or something like that.

**TEACHER:** Alli, you think the number would get bigger. Why?

**ALLI:** 'Cause tenths would be small. There would be a lot of them, but I can't tell how many.

**TEACHER:** What do we need to learn in order to figure out how many? What's hard about this?

**JAMES:** I don't get it. If you times a number by 10, you add a 0 at the end. But if you times a number by .1 (you don't need the 0 after the 1, cause it's a place holder), the number would be the same, cause it's times'd by 1, but it would have to be smaller, 'cause of the decimal.

It was time to end the lesson. I told the class we would talk about this more later and asked them to write in their journals the ideas they have about dividing.

I remember the last time I worked with the students about this concept. At the time, they were unsure how to find the number of thousands in 473,812. This time, they are more confident of their strategies, but unsure of their solution. What questions might I ask to guide these students toward an understanding? What is it they really don't understand about dividing by tens, hundreds, and thousands? Are

Building a System of Tens

their questions related to division, or to place value issues, or both? I really need to think about this for myself before the next lesson.

C A S E   20

# Discussing division

# *Eleanor*

GRADES 3 AND 4, OCTOBER

This case describes my initial discussion of division with a math group of eight- and nine-year-olds. To begin, I wanted to know what the children had to say about the topic itself.

145

TEACHER:     Well, what is dividing?

Mika spoke right up and contributed the first idea.

MIKA:     Taking one number and making it into more than one part. Like 9 into 3 parts.

150

STEPHAN:     Taking a number and splitting it. Like 9 divided by 3, by 2—would be equal. [*pause*] Actually, well, you can't do that.

This idea that dividing is locked into splitting numbers in half seems to keep creeping into discussions as the days go by. Is it a confusion in the way some children visualize division?

155

Jen heard Stephan's confusion and tried to help clarify and articulate his thinking.

JEN:     Split one [a 9] in half so it's 4 and $\frac{1}{2}$. Like there is the 4 and the 4 and then one more, and that would be $\frac{1}{2}$, so it's $4\frac{1}{2}$. [*I know she means that she instantly sees the possibility of dividing an even number, 8, in half, and then the leftover 1 in half, to make $4\frac{1}{2}$.*]

160

MARK:     Sometimes you can't split a number in half. Like 5 pieces of—well, metal or something.

# Eleanor

TEACHER: Well, how about chairs? Take 5 chairs.

MARK: Yeah, like if there were 5 chairs and we [*pointing to his neighbor*] both wanted them, it wouldn't work. If you can split it in half, it's like dividing.

TEACHER: Sagel, you were teaching Stephan your strategy for dividing by 2 the other day. Can you talk about your system?

SAGEL: I think it was 74, but let's say you had 8 and you divided it, so I would draw a line and call it 1, and here, and call it 2, and here, and call it 3, and 4, 5, 6, 7, 8.

Sagel demonstrated the strategy, drawing tally marks on the board, alternating between two rows:

    |  |  |  |
    |  |  |  |

At this point I decided to give the group a problem and see what would happen. I asked them to divide 364 by 2. I thought that giving the children a large number might elicit more sorting out than a smaller one, and dividing by an even number would let them start from what they "know" about dividing. Jen went to the board.

JEN: 364, well, I take the 64 away. [*She hides it with her hand and pantomimes putting it on the other side of the board but doesn't write anything yet.*] It's 300. I split $\frac{1}{2}$ of 300 and it's 150. Then I bring back 64 and cut it in half. It's 30 and I put aside the 4. Then that's 2, so it's 182. [*She writes 182 on the board.*]

MARK: She did it exactly the way I do it.

TEACHER: Mark, why don't you try 496 divided by 4?

MARK: First I'll take away 96 so I have 400. Then I'd do what equals 400, so it's 200, and then half of that is 100, so it's 100. Then I have to put back the 96 and divide 90 but that's 50 and 40? What do I do? Um.

Building a System of Tens

JEN:   It's 45.                                                              195

MARK:   Oh yeah, that's what I was going to do. I would add the 5.
But so then I divide 45 in half and it's 22 and [*pause*] $\frac{1}{2}$.
Then I go back to the 6. Six divided by 2 is 3 so it has to
be $2\frac{1}{2}$ — no, I mean $1\frac{1}{2}$. So 45 + 24. [*He has added the   200
$22\frac{1}{2}$ and the $1\frac{1}{2}$ for the 24 on the board.*] It's 69, so all
together it's 169.

After Mark finished, the group talked about adding all the 100s
contained in four 169s and decided that Mark had made a mistake. I
pointed out that, in his long rendition, he added the 45 he had split into              205
$22\frac{1}{2}$, but that was an error.

MARK:   My work is always so messy.

This led to a discussion about recording and how important it is, when
there are so many steps, to make accurate notes about the work so that
steps can be followed or retraced.

JEN:   Well, I write math sentences, but I never write them               210
while I am doing the math because, by the time I write
it down, I have forgotten what was really clear in my head.
My work in my head is really neat, so I wait and write
the math down after I have the answer. Unless I am
drawing a picture.                                                          215

MARK:   I usually just add up everything anyway.

We talked for a minute about the possibility of doing any math
problem by adding. Then I sent them off to work on some other division
problems like the ones we had been doing (64 ÷ 4, 20 ÷ 5, 121 ÷ 3). The
problems were just dividing-for-dividing's-sake problems, though I          220
added something about chocolate chips or numbers of people to put them
in a story context.

Kia broke down and cried when she couldn't divide 30 by 2
because she knows something about "odd numbers can't be split in
two, and if 3 is odd, then you can't do the problem." A new kid in the      225
class, Kia is extremely bright, but she has a lot of math rules in her

head which aren't helping her much. Joel just whispered that he was completely confused. Mika and Jen skillfully divided three-digit numbers by 2, 3, and 4. Sagel and Stephan, the only third graders in the group, happily tossed the discussion of dividing into some deep recesses in their minds and instead added and added away. Mark gnashed his teeth with great spirit while trying to divide something into three groups. His strategy of dividing in half and then half again didn't work well for him. He really wanted to get it, and he pushed and shoved his way through the problem.

The discussion was interesting to me for a couple of reasons. Basically, I didn't like it at first, though in retrospect it feels like a glimpse into the repertoire of conversations that kids can have in the class, beyond discussions of math story problems and strategies for solving them. When I tried introducing "an action"—an operation—as a topic for discussion, I found it extremely difficult to balance and assist the kids in their thinking. The use of the operation was not imbedded in an ongoing problem; the subject was not raised by the kids themselves; and, for the most part, there was a lot of talking into the air from one kid and then another, not enough of a give-and-take discussion *about* something.

So what's the problem? Why does dividing feel like a missing-addend problem, but instead with a missing factor? Some of those kids could go off from that discussion and build on their strategies of dividing. What did they understand that the rest didn't? What allowed them to move forward when the others were so clearly reeling during the problem time we had after the discussion?

For $20 \div 5$, Stephan wrote:

20 divided by 5 = 4. I counted up by 5 and I got 4.

For $64 \div 4$, Joel wrote:

64 divided by $4 = 11\frac{1}{2}$.

I think Joel worked out $6 \div 4 = 1\frac{1}{2}$ and $4 \div 4 = 1$. Then he somehow combined $1\frac{1}{2}$ with 1 to get $11\frac{1}{2}$. For the same problem, Mark wrote:

$16 + 16 = 32 + 32 = 64 \ldots 16$.

Jen's paper showed this work on two problems:

Building a System of Tens

$$64 \text{ divided by } 4 = 16$$

$$\underset{\underset{15}{\uparrow}}{6} \quad \underset{\underset{1}{\uparrow}}{4} \qquad 15 + 1 = 16$$

$$121 \text{ divided by } 3 = 40\tfrac{1}{3}$$

$$12\,1$$

$$33\tfrac{1}{3} \quad 7$$

$$33\tfrac{1}{3} + 7 = 40\tfrac{1}{3}$$

These kids are in really different places. Jen is able to hold onto true quantities, and they remain stable for her. She can see wholes and parts, and the whole picture is extremely clear. She has invented her own algorithms all the way along in math. (Having also taught her at age five, I remember with what great delight and humor she would make jokes at the snack table, substituting the word "eight" for the actual number of crackers, which was four, and calling everything that was really four "eight," just for the fun of it.)

Mark is adding; he is also stuck on dividing as splitting in 2 and powers of 2.

Joel does not appear to read the 6 in 64 as 60 when he gets into the division problem. He has divided 6 by 4 and 4 by 4, but then he just slips the digits together and calls the result $11\frac{1}{2}$.

Stephan is adding and making accurate estimations, but he is not clear about the idea of division as a way of taking numbers apart rather than building them up.

The information I glean from this episode helps me begin to understand what the children are working on. Division is not the most significant investigation at this point for every child in the class. I want to concentrate now on solidifying what numbers are made of and some of the ways in which numbers are organized in their behavior (odd and

270

275

280

285

even in particular), and I can do that while simultaneously reaching
toward division. I know that Jen, Mika, and Mark have a lot to teach each
other. Jen's grasp of numbers and intuitive understanding of factors will
enable her to articulate what Joel may be speculating about. The notion
of chunking numbers into multiples of fives, tens, and hundreds would
be immensely useful to many of the children in the class, and I think
the strategies would spread quickly if the right problems were offered.
We can focus on the idea that the same numbers can stand for different
quantities within the same problem, and on the idea that if you do
something to one side of an equation, you need to do an equivalent action
to the other side of the equation. At the same time, the children can be
investigating the equivalency of operations and gaining fluency in those
manipulations of number.

   The following day we had parent conferences, and the number
of parents whose children had come home and talked about this
new idea named "division" was remarkable and surprising—especially
because they spoke so positively! Joel's father said that, the night
before, he had watched Joel solve a problem. Shaking his head, he said,
"And there was this kid, sitting at the kitchen table, quietly inventing
long division."

290

295

300

305

C A S E   21

# Sharing jelly beans

*Janie*

This week I decided to see what my fourth-grade students knew about
division. I plan to concentrate more on division later in the year, but at
this time thought I would just see what they already knew. I decided to
throw out a problem and see how they tackled it.

310

 How would you divide 134 jelly beans among 6 kids?

I told the students to pay particular attention to *how* they tackled this problem, and to write about some of the strategies they used. I asked them to work alone so we could see how many different strategies we could come up with. There was a wide range of strategies at the end of the period.

315

Some children drew pictures of 6 kids and, one by one, split up all 134 jelly beans.

José started with 100 beans and divided them up into groups of 25, "but this was only 4, so I kept going down until I had enough for 6 kids." He didn't say how he accounted for the other 34.

320

India first estimated how many each person was going to get, and then turned around and used the regular division algorithm.

Jamie started by giving each kid 10 jelly beans, then gradually increased each kid's share.

325

Mario first multiplied $6 \times 20$, and that gave him 120. Then he multiplied $6 \times 2$ and added 12 more for a total of 132. Then he divided the 2 extra jelly beans into 6 pieces and each kid got $22\frac{1}{3}$.

Most of the students grouped the jelly beans or estimated rather than doling them out one by one. I was pleased with that. I was also pleased at how many decided to try to split the last 2 jelly beans, rather than just disregard them.

330

April's strategies interested me and I wanted to hear more about how she tried to solve the problem. She started off by saying that "you have to know multiplication." She said that her first strategy was to pick a number and count up with it, but her second strategy was to put a two-digit number times 6 and see what the answer would be. I asked April to explain how she decided on a two-digit number, but she couldn't get past telling me the correct answer (22) and how that worked into the 134. To try to understand her thinking a little better, I asked her to work on another problem so she could talk a little more about how her strategy developed. I gave April the chance to pick a division problem, and she decided to use jelly beans again and make the problem a little harder:

335

340

 Divide 143 jelly beans among 8 kids.

345

I asked April to tell me first what she did when she was dividing. She said that division was putting things into groups. "You have to multiply the things to get the groups—like take 8 times any number and see what the answer is." She began her strategy by saying that she knew each kid would get more than 10 jelly beans because that would be 80, and that if each kid got 20 jelly beans, that would be 160, which was too much. So she knew two things: that 10 was too small and 20 was too big. I asked if she thought the correct number would be closer to 10 or closer to 20. She said she thought it would be around 14, and proceeded to multiply $14 \times 8$ to get 112. She then said that you had to add 31 more.

I could tell that she was getting confused with all the numbers, so I tried to make it easier for her by setting up a system to keep track of them:

| 10 | 14 | 20 |
|---|---|---|
| 80 | 112 | 160 |

She then decided to try $22 \times 8$ and got 176. She said she knew she had to try a number that would bring her close to the 160 mark, but lower.

April now decided to "bag" this idea and came up with another strategy—to see how many eights were in 100, and then how many eights were in 43—to see if that worked. Her process:

$10 \times 8 = 80$, $11 \times 8 = 88$, $12 \times 8 = 96$ (with 4 left)

$5 \times 8 = 40$ (with 3 left)

The next part she struggled with. She was losing her train of thought and was confused by all the numbers she had just generated. I tried to help her sort out what she had done by showing her that she had found 12 groups of 8 in 100 and 5 groups of 8 in 40, and that in both cases she had numbers left over. I asked her to think about how many groups of 8 she had. She had 17 groups of 8 (which totaled 136) with 7 jelly beans left over. Good.

Then she came up with a way to divide up the 7 extra jelly beans. She took 4 of them and divided each in half, so each of the 8 kids got $\frac{1}{2}$. Then she had 3 left over, so she took 2 of those and divided them into fourths, so each kid got an additional $\frac{1}{4}$. Then she divided the last jelly bean into eighths, so each kid got another $\frac{1}{8}$.

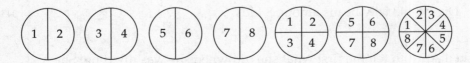

Building a System of Tens

Now the question was, How much was $\frac{1}{2} + \frac{1}{4} + \frac{1}{8}$? This is how she solved that problem:

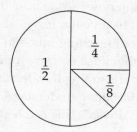

April was delighted when she saw that $\frac{1}{8}$ was left over; she immediately knew that the total was $\frac{7}{8}$. In the end, each kid got $17\frac{7}{8}$ jelly beans.

I was impressed with April's strategies and with how well she could explain what she was trying to do. I was impressed by her ability to change strategies when one didn't seem to be working for her. I was also impressed with the ease with which she was able to combine the fractions, even though we hadn't done much of that in our fraction unit.

The next day, Jorge came in with a problem that he said his father wanted us to try—a special challenge. I'm not sure if it was really his father's problem, but we accepted the challenge. His problem was 1007 divided by 9. At first the problem seemed difficult, but within a few minutes, *many* of the children solved it. Juanita was proud of her strategy and explained it to the class: She knew that $100 \times 9 = 900$ and that $10 \times 9 = 90$, so that took care of 990. She then added one more 9, for 999, which gave everyone 111 jelly beans to start with. She now had 8 more, which she divided into *ninths*, and arrived at her answer of $111\frac{8}{9}$.

I was surprised at how natural this process was for these students. In the past, I would have taught the traditional algorithm, which would have given them little in the way of understanding. Now they had their own methods, many of which involved dividing things up into large chunks first, then gradually decreasing the size of the chunks. Some still struggled with smaller numbers, and it was awkward dealing with the different levels in the class, but they were still arriving at the answer *their* way and with a greater understanding of the process. By observing their processes and listening to their strategies, I feel that most have a very good understanding of what division involves, and have a variety of means available to them to help solve this type of problem.

# Janie

My question now: At what point do I teach them a shortcut—or do I? Do I encourage them to invent their own algorithm? Or do I leave them to refine the methods they are using now? Do I show them the method by which I learned division (and taught division for most of my teaching days—and, oh yes, I agree—without teaching much in the way of under- standing), or do I continue to let them use their own process in spite of how slow it may be? I know the philosophy; I understand the philosophy; I agree with the philosophy. But once they understand the concepts, is there ever a place for the traditional way? This is a real question.

Now that our testing period is finally over, we are back to work on division again. I still feel the need to simplify the students' process of division, and I am still torn about introducing the traditional algorithm as a means to do this. This week I told my class about this dilemma. I told them that the way I learned to do division in my elementary grades did not help me at all understand what I was doing, and that I wanted them to come up with a way (or several ways) I could teach a division algorithm in the future that would let kids understand division. I gave them another problem and asked them to work on it—first individually, and then with a partner, if they wanted to.

Andy seemed very restless and uninterested in the task, so before he disrupted the work of his group, I asked him if he and I could work together. I asked him to think about the problem while I got everyone else started. When I returned to work with him, he said he was thinking about doing the problem 453 ÷ 6 as a bar graph. I had no idea what he was getting at, but he drew a chart with six columns.

I was interested to see how Andy was going to use his "bar graph." He told me that next he was going to draw pictures of the hundreds, tens, and ones using "those place-value blocks." Below the chart, he drew something like this:

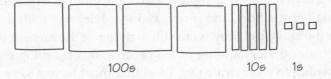

After Andy drew his pictures, he realized that he couldn't give each of the 6 people 100, so he split each of the hundreds into 50 and 50. When he gave each of the 6 kids 50, he wrote this information on his chart.

Building a System of Tens

| 50 | 50 | 50 | 50 | 50 | 50 |
|----|----|----|----|----|----|
| 1 | 2 | 3 | 4 | 5 | 6 | Number of kids

I could now see how he was using his "bar graph"—not a bad way of organizing his numbers! This took care of 300; he now had 100 + 50 + 3 left to divide up. He proceeded to cut the last hundred into tens; he now had 10 tens + 5 tens + 3 ones. He knew that with 15 tens, he could give each kid 2 more tens, so he added this to his chart.

Andy now had 3 tens and 3 ones left. He said that 3 tens equals 30, and 30 divided by 6 is 5, so he gave each kid 5 more and added this to the chart. He now only had 3 left, so he split each in half and gave each kid $\frac{1}{2}$ more. Looking back at the chart, he could now say that each kid got $75\frac{1}{2}$. (Notice that he personalized the problem—at first he didn't talk about a context, but now he talked about each kid getting a certain amount.)

| $\frac{1}{2}$ | $\frac{1}{2}$ | $\frac{1}{2}$ | $\frac{1}{2}$ | $\frac{1}{2}$ | $\frac{1}{2}$ |
|----|----|----|----|----|----|
| 5 | 5 | 5 | 5 | 5 | 5 |
| 10 | 10 | 10 | 10 | 10 | 10 |
| 10 | 10 | 10 | 10 | 10 | 10 |
| 50 | 50 | 50 | 50 | 50 | 50 |
| 1 | 2 | 3 | 4 | 5 | 6 | Number of kids

Several other children in the class arrived at similar solutions, but I thought Andy's way of organizing information was interesting. Many had to struggle to keep track of their numbers. When we shared strategies, the children liked Andy's method as much as I did.

I was hoping that someone would come up with a system of doing
these division problems that was similar to the conventional algorithm
(that is, the way I learned it and the way I've always taught it before), but
I don't think they were ready for that yet.

At this point I am again stuck. How much do I tell? I feel like I can't
take extra risks with these kids. What will their teachers say when they
go on to middle school? So do I lead them to inventing a new algorithm,
or do I teach the old method, or do I leave it as it is? The children seem
to understand what they are doing, but the process is long. They are
becoming more organized in their thinking and more interested in the
methods the other kids are using. One person even asked if everyone
could give a report on "their way." I was surprised at how attentive they
were when Andy slowly explained his strategy and several of the others
followed with theirs. They seemed truly interested. Even when it took the
whole math period to go over three strategies, they still wanted to hear
more and invent new ways.

The children eagerly took their problems home for homework. "Can
we write about our ideas once we figure them out?" someone asked as
we left the room together. That sure warmed my heart!

C A S E  22

# Making sense of division

## Maeve

Over the past few weeks, my fourth graders have begun work with
dividing larger numbers in various contexts. The majority of the students
recognize that the situations represent division situations, but most (if not
all) are using repeated subtraction strategies to solve the problems. This
meaning of division, while effective with smaller quantities, proves to be
inefficient and potentially error-laden as the size of the numbers in the
problem increases. It seems to me that while division and subtraction are
related, students need to examine the connections between multiplication

455

460

465

470

475

480

and division in order to subtract multiples of the divisor and increase efficiency.

I decided to test out some ideas with one of my students, Lexie. She tends to be very articulate and willing to explore. I wanted to think with her about subtracting out "chunks" and consider how this connects to the notation of a standard division algorithm. When I met with Lexie, I began by posing the problem 12 ÷ 4.

|  |  |
|---|---|
| TEACHER: | We are going to step back a little bit from what we've been doing in class to think about what it means to divide. The problem I want you to think about is 12 divided by 4. Could you show how you would use the pieces to do that? |
| LEXIE: | You could take 12 tiles and deal them out into groups of 4. Then keep on doing that. |
| TEACHER: | Are you dealing them into groups of 4? |
| LEXIE: | No, into 4 different groups. I give them out one at a time, and they each get 3. The answer would be 3 because there are 3 tiles in each group. |
| TEACHER: | OK. So that's one way to think about division, you can think about it as dealing. What is another way that I might think about division? |
| LEXIE: | Well, if it is an easy problem, like 12 ÷ 4, you could count by fours until you get to 12: 4, 8, 12 [*putting up one finger for each group*]. I counted by four, um, 3 times, so that would get 3 again. |
| TEACHER: | OK, so you are counting by fours, 4, 8, 12, and you're saying that is 1 finger, 2 fingers, 3 fingers, each finger representing a group of 4. You said something about only doing that on easy problems. |
| LEXIE: | Well, I was thinking that it might take a little bit longer if you do it with your fingers on a big problem like 369 divided by 3. [*Lexie had spotted the problem I had recorded on an index card.*] That will take a lot longer. |

# Maeve

GRADE 4, MARCH

TEACHER: Would it work to do that?

LEXIE: Yes, it would, but I might lose track and it would take a while. 515

TEACHER: So, you'd have to find a way of keeping track of all those numbers. The other way you said you could solve a division problem was to put tiles into groups. Could you use that method on the problem 369 divided by3? 520

LEXIE: You would just deal it out into three different groups until you used all 369 tiles.

TEACHER: What do you think would happen if you use the base ten pieces for that problem?

LEXIE: You could take three hundreds, six strips that equal ten, and 525 then you could take nine units [*building the collection as she describes it*]. First, I'd put 100 in each group. Then maybe you could take the strips and deal them out into the three different groups until you can't deal them out any more. Then you could do the same with the units. Then you get 530 123 [*see Figure 5.1*].

TEACHER: What do you think about that method for solving the problem?

LEXIE: It works.

TEACHER: Do you remember yesterday when we were solving those 535 longer multiplication problems, and we talked about ways that you might show your smaller steps along the way, using numbers and math symbols?

LEXIE: Is there a way to do that on these?

110                                                    Building a System of Tens

## Maeve

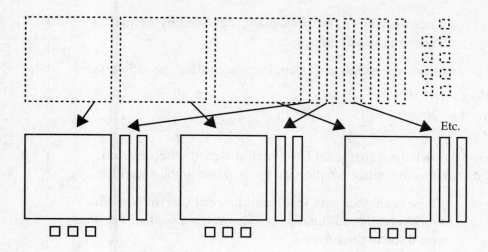

**Figure 5.1** Lexie's plan for using base ten pieces to divide 369 by 3.

| | | |
|---|---|---|
| TEACHER: | Let's think about what it might look like to represent this problem in some way. Why don't you talk me through how you just did this problem. You don't need to divvy them up again. Just talk me through your process. | 540 |
| LEXIE: | Since it's 369, I take three 10-by-10 pieces and give one to each. | 545 |
| TEACHER: | One what? | |
| LEXIE: | One mat in base ten, so 100. Then you deal out the 6 strips to the groups, the 60, by giving one to one group, one to the next, one to the next, until I'm done. | |
| TEACHER: | OK. I'm going to grab this 60 all in my hand. Is there a way that you could just look at them and know what to put in each group? | 550 |
| LEXIE: | Well, if there are three groups, 3 plus 3 equals 6. So that would be two 3s still – two go into each group. | |
| TEACHER: | It seems like you wouldn't have to give out the pieces one at a time, you could give them out in chunks. Like you just gave 20 to each of the groups. Now, talk me through the last part. | 555 |

| LEXIE: | Since there is 9 in the ones place, 9 divided by 3 equals 3. Three go to each group. | 560 |

As Lexie was talking through each step, I was recording the following:

$$300 \div 3 = 100$$
$$60 \div 3 = 20$$
$$9 \div 3 = 3$$

Lexie acknowledged that what I recorded matched what she said. Then I decided to introduce notation that was closer to the algorithm.

TEACHER: There is another way that I could record this thinking that works well for all division problems. It's a method I'm sure you'll see in the future.

LEXIE: Is there a way that I can do it without manipulatives?

TEACHER: Do you remember how we've talked before about having an image in your head for what is happening in a problem, so you know why you are recording what you are?

LEXIE: Uh-huh.

TEACHER: I want to make sure we can connect what you were doing with the pieces, so that when you look at the numbers you say, "Oh yeah, this is because…" even if you don't use the pieces to find the answer. Does that make sense?

LEXIE: Yeah.

TEACHER: So, first you took 300 out of that group of 369, and that left you with 69 [*recording the process as shown in Figure 5.2 as the conversation continues*]. What did the 300 represent?

LEXIE: The number in the hundreds column.

TEACHER: The 3 in the hundreds column. So this [*pointing to the 300*] was like 3 groups of 100. [*Lexie nods.*] I'm just going to write 100 over here to keep track of what you did, or how many you gave to each group. What did you do in the next step?

LEXIE: I took 6 tens and divided them up.

TEACHER: So you took off 60 and those were each groups of …

Building a System of Tens

LEXIE:  Twenty. Then I took the 9 from the ones column and I, um, dealt it out so there was 3 in each group.  590

$$
\begin{array}{r}
123 \\
3\overline{)369} \\
-300 \quad 100 \\
\hline
69 \\
-60 \quad 20 \\
\hline
9 \\
-9 \quad 3 \\
\hline
0
\end{array}
$$

**Figure 5.2**  Recording Lexie's thinking in more traditional notation.

TEACHER:  OK. So you could write "subtract 9." Then, you could look over here [*pointing to the right-hand side*] where we kept track of the size or amount that you gave to each of the groups, which was 100 and 20 and 3, or 123.  595

Lexie indicated that she was following, so I gave her another problem.

TEACHER:  Why don't you try another? How about 844 divided by 4?

LEXIE:  Well, you take…

TEACHER:  Would you like to use the pieces?

LEXIE:  Yeah. No, no, actually not. You take 8 pieces and you maybe put 2 into each group.  600

TEACHER:  How did you decide to do that?

LEXIE:  I don't know. Oh, 8 divided by 4. So 800 equals 200. And 4 divided by 4 would be 1. So 40 equals 10. And 4 divided into 4 groups again would be 1. So, 4 equals 1. That means it would be 211.  605

Lexie completed a lot of work in her head, and her recording method is shown in Figure 5.3 (left). I suggested that someone might look at her paper and wonder, "What is she thinking when she says 800 equals 200?" I suggested that another way she could communicate her thinking about the division was to record what is shown in Figure 5.3 (right).  615

## Maeve

| | |
|---|---|
| $800 = 200$ | $800 \div 4 = 200$ |
| $40 = 10$ | $40 \div 4 = 10$ |
| $4 = 1$ | $4 \div 4 = 1$ |

**Figure 5.3**  Working on a better way to record Lexie's thinking.

It was interesting to consider the decomposition and rearranging that Lexie was seeing to complete the division (that is, $800 \div 4 = (8 \times 100) \div 4 = (8 \div 4) \times 100 = 200$). I opted not to point out this recording of her full process.

Next, I posed a problem that would challenge Lexie's strategy because the number of hundreds was smaller than the divisor: $639 \div 9$. She quickly recognized that the method she had been using would need to be refined. I suggested that since this problem was a little different, maybe she would want to use the base ten pieces again to keep track of her thinking.

Lexie's mind was moving quickly as she imagined cutting up the mats into smaller parts. She suggested cutting them into two parts and counting by twos 6 times (two parts for each of the 6 mats). Then she realized that made 12. She told me that wouldn't work because she would have 3 left over if she dealt them out. Next, she thought she could divide each mat into four parts, giving her 24 parts, but then after giving each group two parts, she would have 6 left over. Next, she decided to divide each mat into three parts. This created 18 parts that she could divide equally among 9.

TEACHER:  How are you going to divide 100 into 3 parts?

Lexie grabbed the strips and traded a mat for 10 strips, then began dealing the pieces into three groups. She gave two strips to each group to begin and saw that there were four left over. Next she said, "I could cut all these in half and that would be 10, so this would be a complete fraction." Then she realized that she could actually give one more strip to each group and trade the other strip in for units. She progressed to giving each of the three groups 33 and had a remainder of 1.

TEACHER:  I want to go back for just a minute. How did you decide to divide each of the mats, or the one hundreds, into three parts?

LEXIE:  Because if I can divide them up, then I could divide by 9, or make the 9 groups.

Building a System of Tens

TEACHER: I think, if I understand correctly, you decided that if there were three groups inside here [*pointing to one mat*], then 3, 6, 9, 12, 15, 18 [*counting three groups in each of six mats*], that would mean there are 18 groups in all of these, and 18 divided by 2 is 9.

650

LEXIE: Wait, why am I having three then?

TEACHER: That's what I was asking about. I think what you are doing is possible, but it's pretty complicated. [*Laughter.*]

655

Lexie continued to explore some different ideas around this for a few minutes. Then she said, "I think I got off track somewhere. I don't know where I am. I am totally lost." I suggested that maybe we could take a look at a different idea and then come back to this problem. There was some hesitation, but she agreed. I thought it might be helpful to look at an array, or an area model, to represent the division.

660

TEACHER: When we first talked about the meaning of division, you had two different ideas. You didn't talk about division using an area model. How might you think about the original 12 divided 4 problem as an area model?

665

Lexie quickly built this model.

TEACHER: Now, as you look at 12 divided by 4 as a rectangle, what do you notice? Where do you see the 12? Where do you see the 4? Where do you see the answer?

LEXIE: Well you go, 3 here [*pointing to the side*], and 4 across here, and it is all 12.

670

TEACHER: What if we tried to build an area model for 639 divided by 9? If we think about this smaller problem here, 12 divided by 4? Do you think you could use an area model to solve 639 divided by 9?

675

LEXIE: Yeah, after I split them all up into groups.

TEACHER:    What kind of groups would you need to make?

LEXIE:      I would need to take 639 tiles and split them up into 9
            groups. What if I count by nines? ... 9, 18, 27, 36, 45, 54, 63,
            72, 81, 90... that's all I know.                                    680

While Lexie listed the multiples of nine, I recorded them in a table (see
the first row of figure 5.4).

TEACHER:    Do you remember yesterday when we were talking about
            multiplication, how sometimes it's helpful to look at 10 times
            the number? [*Lexie nods.*] What if I were to write 90, 180, 270,  685
            360... [*writing the second row in Figure 5.4*]? What does the
            90 represent?

| *9 x 1* | *9 x 1* | | | | | *9 x 7* | | |
|---|---|---|---|---|---|---|---|---|
| 9 | 18 | 27 | 36 | 45 | 54 | 63 | 72 | 81 |
| *9 x 10* | *9 x 20* | | | | | *9 x 70* | | |
| 90 | 180 | 270 | 360 | 450 | 540 | 630 | 720 | 810 |

Note: Italic expressions added during the subsequent conversation.

**Figure 5.4**    A table to help think of 639 divided by 9 in larger chunks.

LEXIE:      It's 9 times 10.

TEACHER:    How about 180?

LEXIE:      9 times 20.                                                         690

TEACHER:    How do you know?

LEXIE:      If 9 times 2 is 18, then 9 times 20 is 180 because it's
            10 times larger.

TEACHER:    How did you get 63?

LEXIE:      It was 9 times 7.                                                   695

TEACHER:    Where do you think the 630 came from?

LEXIE:      It would be 9 times 70.

| | |
|---|---|
| TEACHER: | These are all numbers that I would run into if I kept counting by nines. Do you have some ideas about how you might use this chart to help you find the answer to the 639 divided by 9 problem? |
| LEXIE: | Since 9 times 70 is 630, and 9 times 1 is 9, that would make the 639. So 71? |
| TEACHER: | How were you thinking about the 71? |
| LEXIE: | Um... It's like there are 9 groups of 71 in 639. |
| TEACHER: | I wonder if we could record your thinking using a strategy like I showed you earlier [*pointing to the method recorded in Figure 5.2*]. |
| LEXIE: | I think so. |

700

705

Her method is recorded in Figure 5.5.

$$
\begin{array}{r}
71 \\
9\overline{)639} \\
-630 \quad 70 \\
\overline{9} \\
-9 \quad 1 \\
\overline{0}
\end{array}
$$

**Figure 5.5**  Lexie's use of more traditional notation to record her thinking.

I thanked Lexie for taking the time to share her thinking with me and let her know that her ideas really helped me think about what we might want to explore next. And now it's time for me to ponder. What have I learned from Lexie, and what ideas do I want to bring to the class?

710

C H A P T E R

# 6

# Place value representation of numbers less than 1

| CASE 23 | Tenths and hundredths | Henrietta, Grades 6 and 7, October |
| CASE 24 | Parts of pennies | Margot, Grade 7, September |
| CASE 25 | Paragraphs, sentences, words… | Nicole, Grade 5, November |
| CASE 26 | Why do we need rules? | Nicole, Grade 5, January |
| CASE 27 | Adding tenths to tenths and hundredths to hundredths | Nicole, Grade 5, March |

How does the base ten structure of the number system translate across the decimal point? The cases in chapter 6 were chosen to explore this question. As you read these episodes in which students try to understand decimals, take notes on these points:

■ How do students employ their understanding of whole numbers, and how do their ideas about place value extend to places smaller than 1?

■ What new concepts do they need in order to understand what decimals are and how they function?

119

CASE **23**

# Tenths and hundredths

## *Henrietta*

GRADES 6 AND 7 (SPECIAL ED), OCTOBER

I have been thinking about how complicated decimals are for my
special-needs students. In my class, we have been working with
manipulatives to explore decimal place value and addition of decimals.
One boy, Steven, has been having a lot of difficulty. I met with him a
couple of days after school this week to review reading, building, and       5
adding decimals.

We begin with .25 + .6. Steven reads this problem to me as 2 tenths and
5 hundredths and 6 tenths. When I prompt him to read the first number
again, he is confused. "You mean write it in words?"

I assume he is referring to past math classes in which we read            10
decimals written out in words, and then wrote them as decimal numbers.
I ask if he can read .25 as one decimal number. This is a recurring
difficulty for Steven. He seems to be able to separate the tenths and
hundredths, but not easily read them as one decimal number, 25
hundredths.                                                               15

Steven now proceeds to build the problem. He pulls out 2 tenth-rods
and 5 hundredth-cubes.

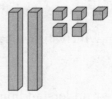

Then he counts out 6 hundredth-cubes.

120

He reports that his answer is 2 tenths and 12 hundredths. I urge him to count again. He puts one hundredth-cube back in the box, and writes out the problem this way:

```
  .25
+ .6
-----
.211
```

Steven reads his answer: "It's 2 tenths and 11 hundredths." I suggest he look again at the original problem and reread it to me. "Two tenths, 5 hundredths, and 6 tenths. Oh!" Steven removes the 6 hundredth-cubes and replaces them with 6 tenth-rods. The total now looks like this:

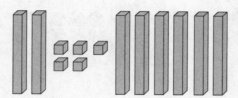

He counts his rods and cubes and says, "It's 8 tenths and 5 hundredths." I write .85 and ask if there is another way to read it as hundredths. Steven is confused again, but finally gets the idea that I want him to assume that his answer is built out of hundredth-cubes. But he doesn't have any idea why. He counts by ones to 80 on the rods, then counts 81 up to 85, and writes:

```
  .25
+ .6
-----
 .85
```

The next day, Steven returns to my room after school and works on the problem .39 + .4. He reads the problem as "3 tenths, 9 hundredths, and 4 tenths," and builds the following:

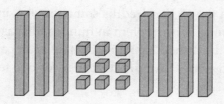

# Henrietta

I ask him if he could reread the .39 as if it were built entirely of hundredth-cubes. He counts each unit on a rod by ones up to 30, then by ones from 31 to 39. "Thirty-nine hundredths," he says, and writes:

$$
\begin{array}{r}
.39 \\
+ \ .4 \\
\hline
.79
\end{array}
$$

"The answer is 7 tenths and 9 hundredths," Steven tells me.
For .28 + .37, Steven builds:

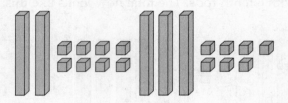

He writes:

$$
\begin{array}{r}
.28 \\
+ .37 \\
\hline
.515
\end{array}
$$

I ask if he can trade in some rods or cubes to show the answer with fewer pieces. He replaces 10 hundredth-cubes with one rod, writes .65, and says, "6 tenths and 5 hundredths."

Again I ask if he can say the number in hundredths. He laboriously starts counting by ones on the rods. "Is there an easier way to count them?" I ask. He suggests counting by twos. We count by twos to 60.

Then he decides to count by tens to 60 and by ones from 61 to 65: "Sixty-five hundredths."

For his final problem, 2.15 + 1.90, Steven attempts to count wholes and hundredths. He lays out 2 whole flats and 15 hundredth-cubes, then 1 flat, and industriously begins counting out hundredth-cubes to 90. I wonder if our working on the 65 hundredths somehow has impressed upon him that he has to build this problem in hundredths, as well as read it as wholes and hundredths. When I ask him if there is an easier way to build the problem, he trades in 10 hundredth-cubes for one tenth-rod, leaving this grouping for 2.15:

Building a System of Tens

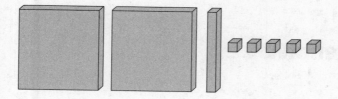

Putting away fistfuls of hundredth-cubes, he builds the following for 1.90:

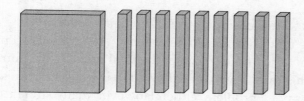

Then he decides to trade again, replacing the 10 rods with 1 whole flat, getting this for the total:

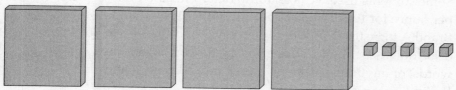

Steven reads his answer as "4 wholes and 5 hundredths." He tells me there are no tenths and writes 4.5 for the answer. After we discuss how to show "no tenths" as a number, he rewrites his answer as 4.05 and reads what he has written as, "4 wholes, no tenths, 5 hundredths."

Steven has many issues about place value and the meaning of number. I wonder about the problem of building with these manipulatives and then translating the physical amount into a single decimal number expressed in the smallest place value. When Steven sees 2 tenth-rods, he doesn't easily see the 20 units within.

# Parts of pennies

## *Margot*
GRADE 7, SEPTEMBER

My seventh graders were working on a unit in their textbook that involved finding the unit price for different items. The students seemed to know the problem called for division of the total price by the number of units, ounces in this case. They were allowed to use a calculator, so the computation was not a problem, either. However, many students were running into a wall trying to decide what the decimal answer on the calculator meant. To get at their thinking, I gave my students this problem:

> Some students used a calculator to determine the price per ounce for two brands of peanut butter. They found Brand A to be 0.09267 dollars per ounce, and Brand B to be 0.967 dollars per ounce. Use grids, pictures, number lines, words, or anything else to *show* how much Brand A and Brand B cost per ounce.

No student represented the thousandth, ten thousandth, or hundred thousandth place in any way. Instead they all rounded to the nearest cent, some correctly and others incorrectly. I was thinking that this happened because the context was money, so students assumed that they should round to the nearest cent. I decided to do some questioning to see if they had ideas about what the amount represented if they didn't round.

My students fell into three main groups: those students who made errors in rounding, students who seemed to grasp that the digits after the hundredths place represented part of a penny, and students who rounded correctly but didn't seem to understand what the numbers in the thousandth, ten thousandth, and hundred thousandth place meant.

This episode describes a conversation I had with Katelyn. She was working to represent the numbers 0.09267 and 0.967. She had drawn pictures of coins to represent her answer of 9 cents per ounce for Brand

## Margot

GRADE 7, SEPTEMBER

A and of 97 cents per ounce for Brand B. She also explained with words why she rounded the way she did, and she colored in squares on 10-by-10 grids (see Figure 6.1).

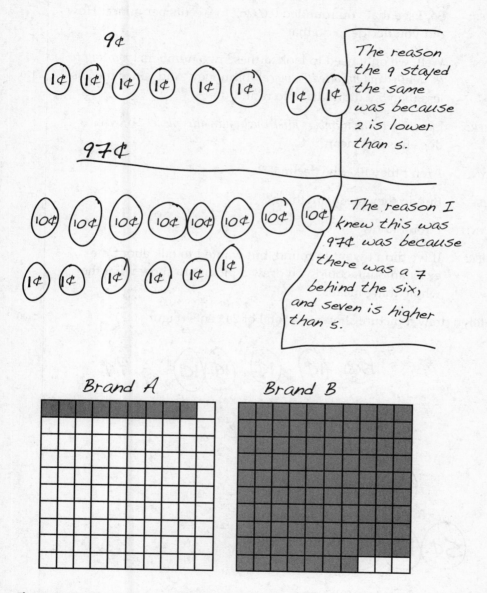

**Figure 6.1**  Katelyn's work to represent the price per ounce of the two brands.

At first glance, I thought Katelyn had a fairly concrete understanding of the decimals she was working with. She seemed to understand that

each small square on the grid could represent one penny, and she told
me that the whole square showed one dollar. However, our conversation
revealed a misunderstanding that was common among my students.

TEACHER: So, I see that you rounded 0.09267 to 9 cents per ounce. How
did you decide to do that?

KATELYN: Well, we only need to look at these two numbers [*pointing to
the tenths and hundredths place*] for money. And, since the 2 is
less than 5, I didn't have to round up.

TEACHER: [*pointing to the numbers after the hundredths place*] So, what
does this 267 mean?

KATELYN: Aren't they like the decimals?

TEACHER: But do they mean anything?

KATELYN: I don't know.

TEACHER: If we didn't want to round, but wanted to talk about the
exact amount, could you draw a picture to show what the
whole thing means?

Katelyn drew a picture showing a total of 24 cents (Figure 6.2).

**Figure 6.2** Katelyn's effort to show 0.09267 cents.

TEACHER: So, is this 2 [*pointing to the 2 in the thousandths place*]
really 2 cents?

KATELYN:     Yeah, well, I don't know.

TEACHER:     So, do you think this number is the same as 24 cents?

I wanted Katelyn to look back at the number 0.09267 and think about the fact that she had rounded it to only 9 cents. Katelyn looked confused at this point and didn't respond. I decided to see if working with the 10-by-10 grids might help. | 135

TEACHER:     So, what if we tried shading squares on the 10-by-10 grids? For 0.09 you shaded 9 squares. For 0.10 how many squares would you shade? | 140

KATELYN:     Ten.

TEACHER:     So how about 0.09267?

KATELYN:     All of the squares?

TEACHER:     So you'd shade all of the squares? | 145

KATELYN:     [*taking a grid and shading as she explains*] First I counted out 9 squares, then 2 squares, then 6 squares, then 7 [Figure 6.3].

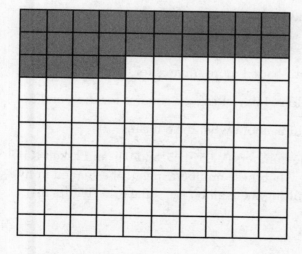

**Figure 6.3**  Katelyn's attempt to show 0.09267 cents on a hundreds grid.

## Margot
GRADE 7, SEPTEMBER

I was struggling to figure out how to make Katelyn's diagram seem problematic to her. She saw 9 squares as representing 0.09, and 10 squares as representing 0.10. But, she didn't seem to have a feel that 0.09267 cents is somewhere between 0.09 and 0.10. In both her picture and grid, she was really representing 24 cents. I was thinking fast to try to come up with some questions to help her see that her answer wasn't reasonable. I decided that 0.09267 was too much for her to think about at the time, so to make the numbers a little friendlier, I wrote down 0.095 and 0.10.

TEACHER:    So which of these is a larger number?

KATELYN:    They are the same because you'd round 0.095 to 0.10.

TEACHER:    Exactly the same?

KATELYN:    Yeah, because you round it up so they are the same. Well, but if we don't round, 0.10 is a little bigger, because this one [*pointing to the 0.095*] was originally a 9.

TEACHER:    Could you show on the 10-by-10 grids what each number means?

On a new grid, Katelyn shaded 14 squares for 0.095 and 10 squares to represent 0.10. I was puzzled that she went back to her original method of shading, even though she had just told me that 0.10 was bigger than 0.095. Where was her understanding breaking down?

TEACHER:    You had told me that 0.10 was the bigger number.

KATELYN:    Yes, it is.

TEACHER:    But you shaded more squares for 0.095.

KATELYN:    Well, don't I have to shade squares for the 9 and 5?

TEACHER:    Let's think about what the 5 means.

I wrote down the numbers 0.005, 0.05, and 0.5, and asked Katelyn if she could show me what these numbers mean. She shaded in five squares for each number, putting them all on the same grid (Figure 6.4).

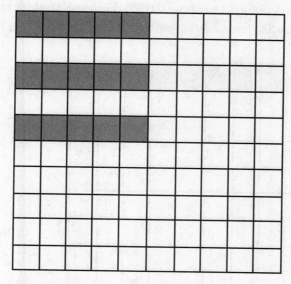

**Figure 6.4** Katelyn's attempt to show 0.005, 0.005, and 0.5 on the hundreds grid

TEACHER:       [*pointing to 0.05*] How much money is this?

KATELYN:       Five cents.

TEACHER:       [*pointing to 0.5*] And how about this?

KATELYN:       Five cents. No! It's 50 cents!

TEACHER:       So how much is 0.005?

KATELYN:       Half a cent? Like, I could shade in half a square?

I felt that Katelyn was just starting to scratch the surface of the idea I was hoping she'd understand. I wanted to go back to 0.095 to see if she would have any more thoughts about that 5 in the thousandths place.

TEACHER:       So what would you shade for 0.095?

KATELYN:       I could shade 9 squares, and then a half of a square.

While I was pleased with her answer, I didn't know how much this idea of a half a square would transfer to other problems. I wondered if she would recognize 0.0925 as being nine and one fourth cents, so I asked her. As Katelyn shaded the grid to show 0.0925 (Figure 6.5), she explained that she shaded 9 squares, then 2 squares, then half a square.

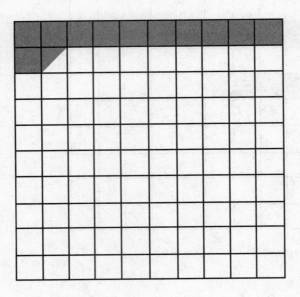

**Figure 6.5**   Katelyn's attempt to show 0.0925 on the hundreds grid

At this point, I really wasn't sure what I could do or ask to help Katelyn understand. We were both feeling a little frustrated and decided to call it a day. A couple of days later, I was still wondering about which misconceptions were getting in the way for Katelyn. It really bothered me that I couldn't think of the right questions to help expand her thinking. Fortunately, a discussion in class that day helped move us all a little forward in our thinking.

We had started talking about percents and how they related to decimals and fractions. Students were discussing how 8.8 percent could be written as 0.088. The conversation went like this:

TEACHER:   How could we shade 0.088, or 8.8 percent?

ANDREW:   You could shade 9 squares, because it is close to 9 percent.

TEACHER:   Yes, we could shade 9 squares, and that would be close, but it's not quite 9 percent. Does anyone have any ideas on how to make a representation that's closer to 8.8 percent?

195

200

205

ALEX:       You could shade 8 squares and then a little more.

TEACHER:    Let's talk more about that idea. How much more?

ALEX:       Maybe about half a square.

YOLANDA:    No, it would be more than half a square, because 8.8 percent
            would mean eight and eight tenths of a square.

ALEX:       Because 0.085 would be eight and a half squares.

AUSTIN:     Oh, yeah! You'd shade 8 squares, and then break the last
            square into 10 little pieces.

ALEX:       And then you'd shade 8 of the little pieces.

At this point the period came to a close, but we all felt that some important thinking had been done. Katelyn was quiet during this conversation, but she seemed tuned in. I'm excited to see how more class discussions like this one will develop her thinking.

# C A S E   25

# Paragraphs, sentences, words . . .

## Nicole

GRADE 5, NOVEMBER

When my students were using calculators to figure averages during our study of statistics, they noticed that many answers included a decimal, sometimes a long or repeating one. They were curious about these strange numbers, and I decided to use their interest to begin a study of decimals, a major portion of our fifth-grade curriculum.

We began by looking back at some word problems we had worked on in the first few weeks of school, with a context involving the students' daily silent reading time. This was one of the problems:

> **?** Rob wants to read one hundred pages of his book before his next conference in seven days. How many pages should he read each day?

When the students had worked on the problem in September, some had divided and found the answer to be 14, remainder 2. Today I asked them to look at the problem again, use their calculators, and see what happens. They agreed that their calculators were reporting the answer in this way:

$100 \div 7 = 14.285714$

I asked them to think about what these two different answers meant. "What's the remainder 2 that we got the first time?" I asked.

Rob responded, "It means you could read 14 pages each day, and you'd still have 2 pages left to read."

Many other children nodded, and Deyon reemphasized Rob's idea saying, "Yes, it's 2 pages."

Jordy added, "It means you could read 14 pages for 5 days, and then read 15 pages on the other 2 days. Then you would get to 100." I was pleased to see Jordy engaged in a math problem. An avid reader, he frequently tunes out during math.

Andrea leapt in to say, "I tried 14 times 7 and I got 98. That means you would still have 2 pages to read." I wondered if Andrea had been paying attention to what the other students were saying, and if she saw any connection to her own idea. She didn't seem to. Rob, however, nodded as if he understood that she was restating the idea he had suggested in the beginning.

Ted waved his hand in the air eagerly. "I did 14 and 2 tenths times 7 and I got 99 and 4 tenths." He didn't offer an explanation for his discovery. However, I realized that he had opened the door for our discussion to move toward reconsidering decimals.

"Then what is the 'point two eight five seven one four' in the calculator answer we got?" I asked.

Quietly, right by my elbow, Sherika said, "The 2 is like a paragraph." Sherika is a talkative and active learner who usually sees the big picture, both in problem-solving situations and in literature. I wasn't surprised that she had such an interesting idea to offer, and I wanted the class to hear and consider it.

"Explain what you're thinking, Sherika," I invited.

"I think the 2 is like a paragraph," she answered. "It's like you need to read 14 pages each day and another paragraph." My mind was spinning as I thought about what Sherika was saying. I was quite sure she was referring to the 2 tenths when she said, "the 2." It seemed like a very powerful interpretation of a decimal remainder in a division problem. I could clearly see the difference between Sherika's idea, in which she was considering the 2 as a portion of a page to be read each day, and the previous ideas, which had suggested that 14 pages be read each day, with the extra 2 pages being read at some point along the way. I wondered if Sherika really knew what she was suggesting.

I invited the class to pursue her idea. "Who would like to restate what you think Sherika is saying and maybe add to it?"

Jeremy's eyes lit up as he raised his hand to volunteer, "I think I get it. In the 14.285714 it's like the 2 is a paragraph and the 8 is a sentence and the 5 is a word and the 7 is a letter and the 1 is half a letter. I don't know what the 4 is. Only the 14 really counts anyway. The other pieces are really small, especially after you get beyond the sentences."

Like Jordy, Jeremy is an avid reader. He isn't as engaged in math as I would like, though he has flashes of understanding that indicate he could be a powerful problem-solver. It interested me that this particular context—their silent reading time—apparently enabled him to conceptualize something that I believed he was, at best, just barely beginning to understand.

His analysis of the problem also reminded me of a context we had explored a few days earlier. I had asked the students if they would rather have 2 and 5 tenths grams of gold or 2 and 33 hundredths grams of gold. In that context, they had begun to refer to the far right decimal places as unimportant. Jeremy himself had taken to referring to them as "dust." He would say, "The numbers closer to the decimal point mean more. The others are just dust; they don't matter." I wondered if he was connecting that context to this one about pages read, and beginning to formulate a general theory for himself.

"That's pretty interesting, Jeremy," I said. "Does it make sense to you that it could work that way?"

"Well, it doesn't *really* make sense," he answered. "I mean, you don't have pieces of words to be read and things like that. It does make sense in some ways though; like how I said, it's really only the first few numbers that make a difference. The rest are too small to matter."

"Did Sherika's idea get you thinking this way?" I asked, musing to myself how often Jeremy lacked sensitivity and appreciation for his classmates.

## Nicole

GRADE 5, NOVEMBER

"Yes!" he responded enthusiastically.

I was pleased that several students had connected their ideas during this lesson, and that we had considered a context that appeared to have significance for many of them. It was exciting that Jeremy, whose ideas in math sometimes lacked connection or relevance to mathematics as a discipline, was able to extend an idea beyond the immediate context to a point at which it still made sense mathematically, even though it didn't make sense in the given context. I began searching for another context that would offer such a fruitful way to consider decimals. I knew I would need a situation, like the reading problems, in which an answer could be interpreted both as a remainder of discrete items and as a decimal with portions of items.

It seemed that we were on our way toward building an understanding of decimals as parts of wholes. I thought we would return to this problem, and to the interpretations offered us by Sherika and Jeremy, as we pursued our investigations.

310

315

320

C A S E  26

# Why do we need rules?

## Nicole

GRADE 5, JANUARY

Over the past few years I have come to believe that it is important for my fifth-grade students to be able to articulate and communicate their understanding of math concepts and solutions for problems. I often give "rule writing" a context by asking how we would communicate what we know about something to someone by telephone, or to a new student who had just entered our class. We regularly engage in such dialogue in class, and I have assumed they understand that being able to communicate ideas in words is an important part of understanding mathematics. A recent class made me rethink that assumption.

One day in January, in our continuing investigation of decimals, I gave each group of four students a pair of numbers similar to these:

325

330

134                                                        Building a System of Tens

# Nicole

GRADE 5, MARCH

| 3.809 | 3.909 |
|-------|-------|

| 3.89 | 3.809 |
|------|-------|

| 38.09 | .3809 |
|-------|-------|

| 38.9 | 38.09 |
|------|-------|

We had been studying decimals for some time, and the class seemed to have a pretty good understanding of how to compare the relative size of two decimal numbers. I asked them to decide which of the two numbers was larger and be ready to present their ideas to the class. Almost every group completed the task quickly, with ease, and correctly.

We posted the number pairs on the board. Next to them I hung "rules" we had written previously for whole numbers. Those rules stated the following:

1. The number that has more digits is larger.

2. If both numbers have the same number of digits or columns, start comparing from the left. The first one that has a higher digit is higher.

I challenged the class to think by saying, "It seemed to be pretty easy for you to decide which of the two numbers was larger. I'm wondering if you used rules to figure it out. Would the rules for decimals be the same as the rules we made for whole numbers?" I asked them to reflect individually, in their notebooks. I suggested it might help to try to think of two decimal numbers that followed the whole-number rules and two that didn't. After a few minutes of quiet thinking and writing, I invited them to share what they had come up with.

Alison tried first. "I know I understand it," she said, "and I think I can say it. First you look at the tenths and hundredths and thousandths and . . . and . . . ." She smiled in frustration that the thoughts in her head were not coming out as clearly as she had hoped.

Casey tried next. "You look at the tenths because they're biggest. It's different than our rules from before. The tenths are biggest."

Luke's hand shot up. "Yeah, I agree with Casey. You look at the tenths. But I don't really know a rule. This is hard."

Javier insisted on talking next. In his usual dramatic way, he rose front and center and used his hands for emphasis. "See, it's like this," he said. "Either one is bigger or the other is bigger or they're equal, and that's it!" Javier seemed almost to be joking about how obvious his statement was. However, it had real mathematical validity.

Chapter 6

335

340

345

350

355

360

365

I responded, "You know, Javier, what you just said is the way mathematicians talk about things. I heard you say that there are only three choices: Either one is bigger, or the other is, or they're equal, right?" Javier grinned in response.

Picking up Javier's idea, J.R. said insistently, "Here's what you know. You assume one of them is bigger. You start with the realization that one must be bigger, so that's that." At this point I sensed that the students were almost backtracking, as if they were trying to find solid ground on which to base their rules. Even though they had devised rules for whole numbers, and operated as if they knew rules for decimals, they didn't seem to be able to go straight to formulating rules. There was frustration in the air, and soon it would erupt.

First we heard from Kelly. She seemed to be referring back to Alison's idea. "I think you look at the whole numbers first because they are biggest. Then you look at tenths and hundredths and thousandths."

Quiet, thoughtful Carlos raised his hand and added, "I agree. You start with the tenths and then go to hundredths."

I asked again, "So what is the rule? Can you say the rule?"

J.R., taking a leadership role uncharacteristic for him in math class, spoke with some exasperation, "I *can't* explain it. Anyway, we don't need a rule because we get it already. It's too hard to say a rule. What's it for anyway? We understand it because we can do it."

Backing him up, Luke—who often delights in reciting rules, even when he doesn't understand them—said, "Yeah. Why do we need a rule? We get it already because we can do it. When you really understand something you don't need a rule for it." I sensed that these two were reflecting sentiments widely held in class at that moment. I thought hard about what they were saying. The positive side of it was that they were emphasizing understanding and saying that when you really understand, you don't need a rule to tell you what to do. The negative side haunted me as I wondered whether they really *did* understand, since they couldn't state a rule for how they were operating, especially given the support of many students working together.

I puzzled through my own confusion by restating what I thought I had heard. "So you're saying that when you really understand something, you don't need a rule for it. That the rule is extra and too much work and you don't need it because you do understand and you know you do." Many children nodded. I realized the irony of their argument. In another

370

375

380

385

390

395

400

setting these students would have been expected to learn rules put forth by their teacher and use them to operate. If they had questioned the rules, the teacher might have said, "You don't need to understand. It's the rule." Now they were insisting that they didn't need rules precisely because they *did* understand.

Later, when I looked over their notebooks, I found evidence that many had been thinking hard and experiencing a good bit of confusion as they worked individually. Many stated clearly that the whole-number rules wouldn't always work. Some gave examples of number pairs in which they worked and others in which they didn't. No one ventured a decimal rule.

I knew I didn't agree with them that rules are irrelevant. I could tell that the thinking we had done together was challenging and confusing to all of us. I realized that something about the word "rule" was irritating to them. I suspected that their own "rules" for comparing whole numbers were not entirely clear to them. Clearly, their concepts of place value were still not solid. I left the topic for that day, but I knew we would return to it often.

###### C A S E  27

# Adding tenths to tenths and hundredths to hundredths

# Nicole
###### GRADE 5, MARCH

In the middle of March, my class returned to the study of decimals after a break of several weeks. I offered a problem that, I hoped, would force them to consider how they could correctly add decimals, including tenths, hundredths, and thousandths.

"Pretend you are a jeweler," I said. "Sometimes people come in to get rings resized. When you cut down a ring to make it smaller, you keep the small portion of gold in exchange for the work you have done. Recently you have collected these amounts." I wrote on the board:

    1.14 g        .089 g        .3 g                          430

"Now you have a repair job to do for which you need some gold. You are wondering if you have enough. Work together with your group to figure out how much gold you have collected. Be prepared to show the class your solution."

I circulated around the room overhearing conversations and thinking    435
about what my students were considering. Nikki said tentatively, "We could line the numbers up on the right like you do with other numbers."

Ned disagreed, suggesting instead, "Maybe we should line up the decimals, but I don't know why we would do that."

"I think you're suggesting that you might line this problem up    440
differently from the way you line up whole-number addition. Is that right?" I asked. Ned nodded, and I continued, "Why do you line whole numbers up the way you do? What's the reason for it?"

"I don't know," Ned answered. "It's just the way you do it. That's how we learned to do it."    445

Malik offered, "I think it would help if we drew a picture, like of the blocks. Maybe we could figure it out then."

In the next group, Rob, assertive, cooperative, and self-confident, said, "I'm sure we should line them up in sections." His groupmates listened, but didn't seem to understand what he was suggesting until he added,    450
"You need to put tenths with tenths and hundredths with hundredths."

In the back corner, Johanna, Jerry, and Jaron had already set up their problem as shown in Figure 6.6.

"What happened to the decimal numbers?" I asked them.

Jaron replied, confidently, "We just decided to drop the decimals and    455
add the numbers like usual. That way we could line them up on the right and add. We left the zero in there, but you can just leave it out since it doesn't mean anything."

"Do you all agree?" I probed.

"Yes," the other two responded, smiling.    460

"Are you saying, then, that if you start out with 1 and 14 hundredths grams of gold and some other little bits that it adds up to 206 grams of gold?" I continued.

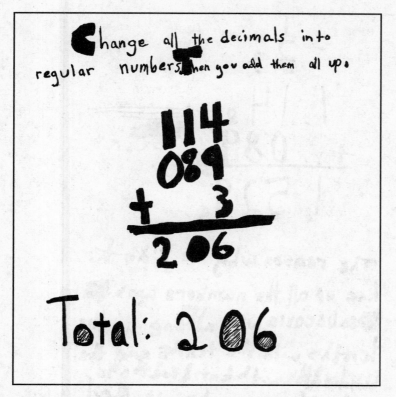

**Figure 6.6** Johanna, Jerry, and Jaron decide to simplify the problem by getting rid of the decimal points.

They seemed a bit puzzled, and looked again at their work, but I was called away to another group.

We had time for only a short discussion before lunch, and the debate centered around whether the correct answer was 1.529 or 2.06. Rob quickly demonstrated his group's solution, as shown in Figure 6.7.

Ned asked, "How did you decide to line the numbers up like that?" Ned is such a strong mathematical thinker that it didn't surprise me that he was still searching for a reason to line up the numbers in the way he had intuitively guessed was correct. Perhaps he was hoping that Rob would give him the explanation he hadn't been able to formulate.

465

470

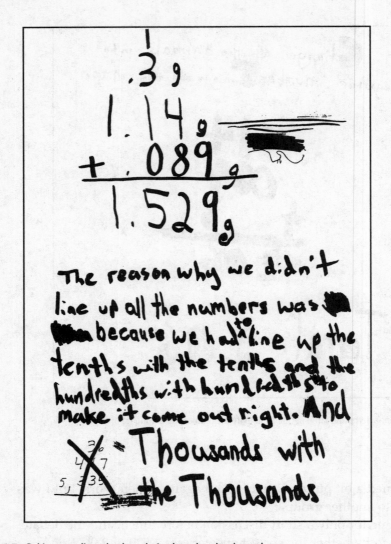

**Figure 6.7** Rob's group aligns the three decimal numbers by place value.

Rob responded, "The reason we did it this way was we thought we needed to line up the tenths with the tenths and the hundredths with the hundredths to make it come out right. You also need to line up the thousandths with the thousandths." That was a more mathematically precise explanation than Rob had offered his group when he had said, "You need to line up the sections."

Nikki wasn't satisfied. She listened and wondered, "I see what you did and why you did it, but our group tried something different, and we got a different answer. Do you think there could be two right answers?" She wasn't truly surprised when he answered, "No. I think there is only one right answer."

Jaron then entered the debate, saying adamantly, "I think your answer is way too big. Our group just dropped the decimals and added. You can also drop the zero since it doesn't stand for anything. We got 2 and 6 hundredths for an answer, and I think that's right."

Teresa, always searching for sense, burst into the discussion with, "What do you mean their answer is too big? Your answer is even bigger!" It was clear at this point that for many students, the motivation to continue the discussion was the search for the right answer. Since the problem had a context and our imaginary jeweler would want to know precisely how many grams she had, any old answer wasn't satisfying them.

Teresa continued with, "Anyway, you can't just drop that zero. It has to be there or you get 89 hundredths instead of 89 thousandths, and they're not the same at all." I knew figuring out this zero question was important, but I decided to sidestep it for now and return to it another time.

I turned and asked Malik to share his idea of how to arrive at a solution. His group had not written anything down, but they had had a very thoughtful exchange, and they were all actively involved in the discussion. He said, "Well, I was thinking it would help if we could draw a picture, like of the blocks. I tried to do it, but I couldn't quite figure it out. If I had the flats be one whole, then the rods are tenths and the units are hundredths, but I don't know how to draw the thousandths except as dots. Then I can't really tell what's going on."

Jaron insisted, "I still say you can drop the zero because it's just nothing."

On the way to lunch, Ben stopped by my desk to say, "I think I know how we could draw a picture. If we use the thousand block to be one whole then we can use the flats for tenths, the rods for hundredths, and we have the units for thousandths."

"Do you think you could do the problem with the blocks then?" I asked him.

"I'm sure I could," he answered.

That afternoon, during quiet reading time, I asked Ben if he wanted to invite Rob and Kwame to work in the hall with him to see if they could demonstrate the problem in the way he had suggested with the blocks.

# Nicole

I thought if Ben could explain it to them, then maybe the three of them
could explain their understanding to the class.

The next day the three boys set up their demonstration. I told the
class that Ben had come up with a way to use the blocks to include
thousandths, and that I thought it might help us pursue the idea that
Malik had proposed, that he could understand it if he could draw it. They
each took a part in explaining what they had done. Their demonstration
with base ten blocks looked like this:

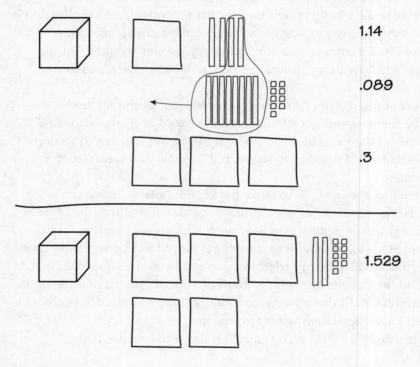

Malik was riveted to the show, listening carefully and nodding.
Teresa also seemed to connect to the explanation, especially realizing
that the zero was very significant in deciding which blocks to use. After
everyone had a chance to observe and ask questions, I asked students to
write in their journals what they thought were the correct procedure and
answer, and what had helped them most to understand. Many students
mentioned that the demonstration had made it clear to them that you
needed to add tenths to tenths and hundredths to hundredths or you
wouldn't get the "right" answer.

Building a System of Tens

## Nicole

GRADE 5, MARCH

I invited them to continue thinking about adding decimals by devising problems of their own. The next day, Andrea and Ned showed up with pages covered with carefully done problems, like the ones in Figure 6.8.

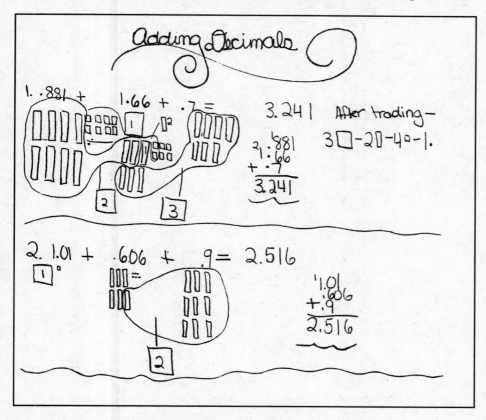

**Figure 6.8** Andrea and Ned use base ten blocks to model addition of decimals.

It seemed that, in this instance, my students' determined search for a right answer had led them to a much deeper understanding of place value, decimals, and addition with decimals of varying places. I was delighted that they cared so much about getting the "right" answer.

Chapter 6

# Multiplying and dividing
# with decimals

| **Case 28** | **Representing decimal products** | *Leslie, Grade 6, October* |
| --- | --- | --- |
| **Case 29** | **Why do we move the decimal anyway?** | *Bernard, Grade 8, December* |
| **Case 30** | **Quotients as decimals** | *Tara, Grade 6, February* |

One of the remarkable things about the place value system is that the same calculation procedure can be used for any pair of numbers, no matter how large or how small. The only question, when dealing with decimals, is where to place the decimal point. The students in case 28 are working on multiplication, exploring what happens when the portions less than 1 are multiplied. In case 29, students are working on division and offer different ways to think about the placement of the decimal point. As you read these cases, consider the following questions:

- How do the whole-number algorithms apply to decimals?

- Why do the rules for placing the decimal points work?

The students in case 30 have come across another issue. When they divide two whole numbers, sometimes the quotient is a decimal that terminates, and sometimes the quotient is a decimal that repeats indefinitely. As you read, consider these questions:

■ What pairs of numbers, when divided, produce terminating decimals?

■ What pairs of numbers, when divided, produce repeating decimals?

C A S E   28

# Representing decimal products

## *Leslie*

GRADE 6, OCTOBER

As my sixth graders and I begin working with the multiplication of decimals, I see that most students can find the products accurately using an algorithm they've learned. Yet, many of these same students have difficulty representing the product with manipulative materials or a diagram. Further, when presented with word problems that are multi-            5
plicative in nature, students sometimes use operations that don't fit the situations and end up with solutions that don't make sense.

All of this became apparent early in our work with decimals, when I posed the following problem, asking students to solve it using both numbers and a diagram.                                                                                       10

> Mr. Smith needs new carpet for one of his rooms. The room measures 11.1 meters by 15.3 meters. How much carpeting should Mr. Smith order?

A few students didn't even see the problem as involving multiplication. They added the two dimensions together, in effect finding half the      15
distance around the room instead of the area of the room. Olivia's work is representative of this misunderstanding. I asked her to explain her strategy to me.

OLIVIA: First I estimated, so I knew I should get a little more than 26 meters. Then I did the actual problem, and I drew the key and the diagram to show how I added (Figure 7.1). My solution is reasonable, based on my estimate.

20

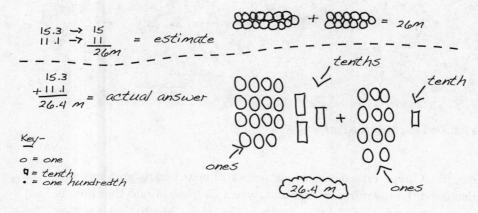

**Figure 7.1** Olivia's work on the carpet problem.

I asked Olivia to draw a picture of the room to show how her calculation would tell Mr. Smith how much carpeting he needs to order. I planned to get back to her later, to see if her picture would reveal to her a problem with her solution.

25

Ceci, like several other students, found the perimeter of the room rather than its area. I asked her to tell me about her work (shown in Figure 7.2).

CECI: First I just added the two numbers together, but when I drew my diagram, I saw that I needed to go around the other two sides of the room. I had only gone halfway. So I doubled the numbers and then added the doubles together. I knew it was square meters because I think it's area. That's how you find area, right? Isn't area what you do with carpet?

30

35

## Leslie

GRADE 6, OCTOBER

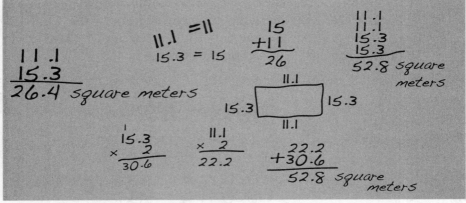

**Figure 7.2**  Ceci's work on the carpet problem.

Ceci, like Olivia, revealed confusion about linear versus area measure. We discussed the meaning of area and, when Ceci explained that area is how many squares it would take to cover the floor, "like the square tiles on the floor here," I suggested that she figure out the number of square tiles on the floor of our classroom. This would open up a discussion about what operation is used to find the area of a rectangle, and whether her calculation for the original problem answered the question of how much carpeting Mr. Smith needed.

Chad seemed to be finished, but when I asked about his diagram (Figure 7.3), he said it didn't make sense.

TEACHER:   What is bothering you about your drawing?

CHAD:   Some of it is missing, but I don't know where it goes.

TEACHER:   Some of what is missing?

CHAD:   Some of the 169.83. I have the 165 that you get from 11 × 15. And I have the 1 tenth and the 3 tenths. But that makes 165.4 altogether, and it's supposed to be 169.83. So over 4 is missing, but I can't figure it out.

148                                                    Building a System of Tens

# Leslie

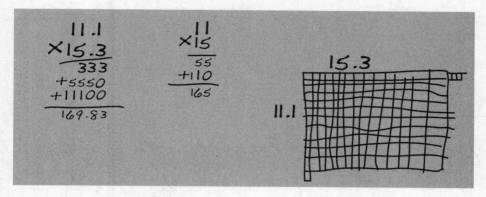

**Figure 7.3**    Chad's work on the carpet problem.

TEACHER:    Do you think you made a mistake with your multiplying?

CHAD:    No, I already double-checked it. It's supposed to be 169.83.

TEACHER:    Are you saying that you think your diagram is missing the 4 and 43 hundredths? [He nods.] You said that know you have all of the 11 × 15. So think about the 1 tenth and the 3 tenths. Maybe if you look at the arithmetic you did, it will help you figure it out. Or maybe your picture will help you. The 3 tenths and the 1 tenth do look different from the rest of the diagram.

I left Chad to ponder his work and moved on to Tori, asking her what she had figured out (Figure 7.4).

TORI:    I think it should be 169.83 carpet meters. I thought at first that I was wrong, because I had all of these tenths at the bottom and on the side, but when I counted them I ended up with 48 tenths. That's 4 whole ones and 8 tenths. Then the other three pieces have to be the 3 hundredths, because that makes it right.

TEACHER:    How do you know those 3 are hundredths?

Chapter 7

149

## Leslie

GRADE 6, OCTOBER

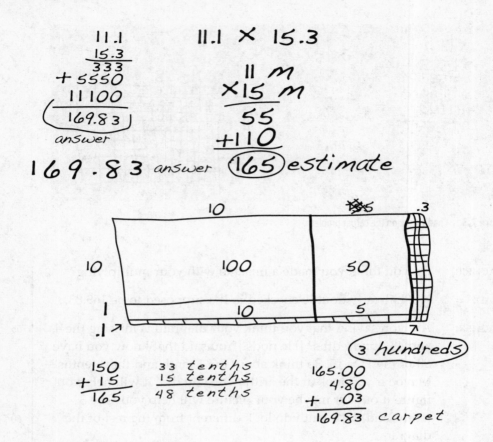

**Figure 7.4** Tori's work on the carpet problem.

TORI: Because when I add the 165 to the 4.8, I get 169.8. I still need 3 hundredths, so the three on the corner have to be those. That's 3 hundredths.

TEACHER: What did you multiply together to get the 3 hundredths? Can you tell in your drawing?

TORI: [*looking and thinking*] Oh, it's from the 0.3 × 0.1. That's what it is! It's 3 tenths times 1 tenth equals 3 hundredths, right?

75

150                                                        Building a System of Tens

| TEACHER: | Is it OK that you are starting with tenths and ending up with hundredths? Is that what's happening? | |
| --- | --- | --- |
| TORI: | I think so. It's kind of like dividing, but you're multiplying. | 80 |
| TEACHER: | What do you mean, it's kind of like dividing? | |
| TORI: | Well, it's like when you divide something, and you end up with a part of it. It's the same thing. When you do 1 tenth times 3 tenths, you don't have the whole 3 tenths anymore. That would be *1* times 3 tenths. But this is *1 tenth* times 3 tenths, so it's got to be smaller than 3 tenths. So it makes sense. | 85 |
| TEACHER: | So 1 tenth times 3 tenths is 3 hundredths? | |
| TORI: | Yes, 1 tenth times 3 tenths is 3 hundredths. | |

Tori's diagram had made sense, but she had decided what those three little boxes were based on her computation. She knew she needed 3 more hundredths to match the product she had, so she had "named" them based on that answer and not on her understanding of what happens when tenths are multiplied by more tenths. Had she really gotten that bigger idea by explaining it to me? I'm not sure.

The carpeting problem I posed brought up new ideas for my students and gave me information about their understanding. It has become clear to me that if we are to use area problems as a context for gaining insight into decimal multiplication, we must first do some work on area and linear measurement. Several students, like Olivia and Ceci, need to see how covering a rectangle with square units is related to multiplication.

The work of Chad and Tori reveal that this context can be fruitful for gaining insight into decimal multiplication. Chad, like several of his classmates, has an image of the array structure of a rectangle whose sides are whole numbers of units in length. They need to see how to extend their representation when the lengths involve parts of units.

Tori has seen that once the diagram is drawn to represent the square units, she can match the parts to the calculation she had already done. She was able to make connections to several notions she had about multiplication and division, thus gaining new insights.

By the way, I was a little surprised that when my students multiplied $15.3 \times 11.1$, no one thought about 11.1 the way that I had anticipated.

## Leslie

I thought they would see 11.1 as a "nice" factor, and I envisioned them breaking it up and using the distributive property:

$$15.3 \times 11.1 = 15.3 (10 + 1 + 0.1) = (15.3 \times 10) + (15.3 \times 1) + (15.3 \times 0.1)$$

115

I wonder why nobody saw it that way.

C A S E  29

# Why do we move the decimal anyway?

## Bernard

I was interested to see how my eighth-grade students think about division with decimals. I presented the problem 49.92 ÷ 15.6, written horizontally on the board. I asked the students not to use calculators.

Almost immediately, three or four students raised their hands to confess that they didn't know what to do. I asked them to try to solve it any way they could think of. All of these students chose to round off the dividend and divisor to solve.

120

After about 5 minutes, I called the class together to discuss strategies. Joey was the first student to volunteer to come to the board. He wrote:

125

$$15.6 \overline{)49.92}$$

| | |
|---|---|
| JOEY: | I just divided it like it was. I started with 3. |
| TEACHER: | What do you mean, you "divided it like it was"? |
| JOEY: | I know you're supposed to do something with the decimal, but I can't remember what, so I just did it without moving it. |
| TEACHER: | I see. May I ask why you started with 3? |
| JOEY: | I know that 4 fifteens are 60 and that's too much. I tried 3 fifteens and got 45, so I tried 3 × 15.6 first. |
| TEACHER: | Did you do 3 × 15.6? |

130

Building a System of Tens

JOEY:       No, I did this. [*He writes out his process on the board.*] Then     135
            I just moved the decimal over one.

$$
\begin{array}{r}
15.6 \\
+\ 15.6 \\
\hline
31.2 \\
+\ 15.6 \\
\hline
46.8
\end{array}
\qquad
\begin{array}{r}
15.6\,\overline{)4\,9.9\,2} \\
-\,4\,6.8 \\
\hline
3.1\,2
\end{array}
$$

                                                                              140

TEACHER:    Why did you do that?

JOEY:       Because when I added earlier, I saw that two 15.6s were 31.2
            and besides, 15.6 won't go into 3.12.

Joey then wrote:

$$
\begin{array}{r}
15.6\,\overline{)4\,9.9\,2} \\
-\,4\,6.8 \\
\hline
3\,1.2 \\
-\,3\,1.2
\end{array}
$$
                                                                              145

TEACHER:    So what did you get as a final answer?

JOEY:       3.2.                                                              150

TEACHER:    Can you explain how you got 3.2?

JOEY:       Well, 15.6 goes into 49.92 three times. Then I knew that 15.6
            went into 31.2 two times because of adding earlier, and I just
            moved the decimal up.

$$
\begin{array}{r}
3.2 \\
15.6\,\overline{)4\,9.9\,2} \\
-\,4\,6.8 \\
\hline
3\,1.2 \\
-\,3\,1.2
\end{array}
$$
                                                                              155

I knew that mathematically there were more questions to ask Joey, but         160
at this point I was just interested in seeing how my students approached
division.

George offered his strategy. He wrote the following on the board:

$$15.6\overline{)49.9\ 2}$$

with quotient 3.2, showing:
- $-46.8$
- $3\ 1\ 2$
- $-3\ 1\ 2$

He explained that he did it like Joey except that he just ignored the decimal in the last step. He wrote 312 instead of 31.2. It was interesting to me that several students approached the problem this way. It did not seem to bother them that there was a decimal in the problem. Do these students have good number sense? Then another student came to the board.

JESSICA: Well, you are supposed to move the decimal over in the divisor. Because you move it once here, you also move it once here. [*She drew arrows as she talked and then rewrote the problem.*] I first tried 156 × 2 and that seemed too low, so then I tried 156 × 3.

$$15.6\overline{)49.9\ 2} \qquad\qquad 156\overline{)499.2}$$

Jessica then did the division problem the traditional way. She also got an answer of 3.2. Looking at Joey's and Jessica's work, I began to wonder why we move the decimal when we divide. Why is it we teach this method? I asked if anyone had another way. Rachel volunteered.

RACHEL: Well, I don't like working with decimals, so I just moved them like this:

$$15.6\overline{)49.9\ 2} \qquad\qquad 1560\overline{)4992}$$

Before continuing her explanation, Rachel then wrote:

| 1560 | 1560 | 1560 |
|------|------|------|
| × 4  | × 3  | × 2  |
| 6240 | 4680 | 3120 |

RACHEL: I first tried 1,560 × 4, but that was too much. Then I tried 1,560 × 3. [*She writes out her long division.*] 1,560 wouldn't go into 312, so I put in a decimal point and added a zero. I got an answer of 3.2.

$$
\begin{array}{r}
3\phantom{0}.2\phantom{.0} \\
1560\overline{)4992\phantom{0}.0} \\
-4680\phantom{.0} \\
\hline
312\phantom{0}0 \\
-\phantom{0}312\phantom{0}0 \\
\hline
\end{array}
$$

It was interesting to see Rachel's strategy. Not only did she initially avoid working with decimals, but she also did not have to worry about what number to "bring down." She was able to subtract all of the numbers at once.

As I looked at my students' strategies on the board, I was wondering what big ideas were hiding there. Why is it that not moving the decimal works? Why is it that moving the decimal works? Mathematically, why are we allowed to do that? I hadn't really thought about the answers to these questions myself. Examining my students' thinking was forcing me to think about the whys. I posed these questions to my students.

TEACHER:     Why is it we move the decimal in dividing?

SHANA:     It makes it easier to work with.

JIM:     My teacher from last year said that's the way you do it.

TEACHER:     Why does it work? Why are we allowed to do that?

FRANK:     Because, what you do to one side you do to the other.

I often hear this explanation from many students when we are dealing with issues of equality and balance. I know that a division problem doesn't have "two sides," but I think Frank is on to something. I have an "aha" moment and decide to lead my class in a specific direction. I push his thinking.

TEACHER:     What do you mean?

FRANK:     Well, you move the decimal one place in the divisor, you have to move it one place in the dividend. If you move it two places in the one, you have to move it two places in the other.

TEACHER:     I see. So, if I have $3 \times 2$, then I need to do the same thing to both numbers?  $30 \times 20$ or $0.3 \times 0.2$  But do I get the same answer for these problems?

## Bernard

JOEY:       No, it's not the same.

TEACHER:    Yet, if I do it with numbers that I'm dividing, I do get the          230
            same answer?

SARAH:      Yes. Look at the problems on the board. We have 49.92 ÷
            15.6, 499.2 ÷ 156, and 4,992 ÷ 1,560, and they all have the
            same answer.

TEACHER:    So, here is something I want you to think about. Why is it            235
            these problems have the same answer of 3.2? Why can we
            move the decimal and get the same result? Why does it work
            for division and not multiplication?

We had reached the end of the period, so that discussion would take
place the following day.                                                         240

C A S E   30

# Quotients as decimals

## Tara

For homework, I asked my sixth-grade students to write decimal word
problems. In class, the students sat in groups of three and exchanged
problems to work through and discuss. The following is a description of
what happened in one group. It started with this problem:

> Mrs. Leonard went to Pinches and Pounds and bought 4.0               245
> pounds of gumballs. She shared them with Ms. Field and Mr.
> McCoy. If each of them got the same amount of gumballs,
> how much did they each get? Were there any left over?

Nanette divided 4.0 by 3 like this:

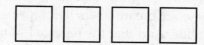

In the beginning of our decimal explorations, I encouraged students to explain their thinking using base ten blocks. We called them decimal squares, letting the flat equal 1 whole, the rod equal 1 tenth, and the unit equal 1 hundredth.

Using the decimal blocks, Charlene explained what she had done. She represented the four pounds this way:

The last decimal block, 1 whole pound, is split into tenths.

"Then take the 1 tenth left over and split that into hundredths. It's supposed to be 1.33 with a remainder of 1," Charlene explained.

Nanette responded, "That's what I got this time when I did the problem. Before, I got 1.3 with a remainder of 1."

$$\begin{array}{r} 1.3 \\ 3\overline{)4.0} \\ \underline{3} \\ 1\,0 \\ \underline{9} \\ 1 \end{array}$$

One of the girls used the calculator and got 1.3333333. Nanette's eyes got big!

An-mei volunteered, "I think it depends on the zeros that you put on the end of the number you are dividing."

Charlene continued, "Like this is 1.3," and wrote:

$$\begin{array}{r} 1.3 \\ 3\overline{)4.0} \end{array}$$

Nanette then suggested, "Put another zero on the end of the number and you get 1.33, and another zero gives us 1.333."

$$\begin{array}{r} 1.33 \\ 3\overline{)4.00} \end{array} \qquad \begin{array}{r} 1.333 \\ 3\overline{)4.000} \end{array}$$

Following my instructions, this group decided to go on to the next problem, putting this exploration aside for the time being. However, as An-mei and Nanette pursued the problem I had given them, Charlene went back to the questions that had been inspired by the first problem. A few minutes later, she had drawn An-mei and Nanette back in, saying, "What I found out is that these are the numbers that repeat—3, 6, and 9—when you use them to divide. And that the repeated number is the number after the decimal point."

Charlene wrote the following to show what she meant:

$$\begin{array}{r} 1.333 \\ 3\overline{)4.000} \end{array} \qquad \begin{array}{r} .666 \\ 6\overline{)4.000} \end{array} \qquad \begin{array}{r} .444 \\ 9\overline{)4.000} \end{array}$$

An-mei responded, "I think it only happens when you divide, not multiply."

After more experimenting with the calculator, Charlene said, "Look! Eight doesn't work."

$$\begin{array}{r} .375 \\ 8\overline{)3.000} \end{array} \qquad \begin{array}{r} .75 \\ 8\overline{)6.00} \end{array} \qquad \begin{array}{r} 1.125 \\ 8\overline{)9.000} \end{array}$$

The group went to work dividing by other even numbers. Initially, they thought that the even numbers did not produce repeating numbers or run-ons, as they called them. Nanette did a few different examples:

$$\begin{array}{r} 2.00 \\ 2\overline{)4.00} \end{array} \qquad \begin{array}{r} 2.25 \\ 4\overline{)9.00} \end{array} \qquad \begin{array}{r} .5 \\ 6\overline{)3.0} \end{array}$$

Then she proposed another theory, and tried it out: "Nine works most of the time, but not always, I think."

$$\begin{array}{r} .222 \\ 9\overline{)2.000} \end{array} \quad \begin{array}{r} .444 \\ 9\overline{)4.000} \end{array} \quad \begin{array}{r} .888 \\ 9\overline{)8.000} \end{array} \quad \begin{array}{r} .555 \\ 9\overline{)5.000} \end{array} \quad \begin{array}{r} .777 \\ 9\overline{)7.000} \end{array} \quad \begin{array}{r} .666 \\ 9\overline{)6.000} \end{array}$$

# Tara

Charlene then added to the theory: "It might work with 3, 6, or 9 as the dividend, but only if the numbers are not the divisor. I think that the numbers only work some of the time because they are divisible by 9."

I am not sure I know what Charlene meant. I think she may have begun to notice something important, but the 42-minute class had come to an end without any resolution to the issue of repeating decimals. The rest of the class had pursued a different task altogether, but the work of these girls really intrigued me. I wanted them to know that I valued their work, and I wanted them to share what they had done with the class.

About a week later, I asked An-mei, Nanette, and Charlene to explain to the whole class what they had discovered. Each person in the class was given a calculator, and the three girls went to the board and explained what they had seen about repeating decimals. The class had time to ask questions of this group and help find some more pairs of numbers that make repeating decimals. This gave all of us, including me, the chance to catch up to the work that An-mei, Nanette, and Charlene had done.

We are not finished, but when I watched these three students take over the math class, it was one of those "teaching moments" that happens every now and then. The class was impressed with their discovery. I was pretty amazed, too!

I think when we return to the idea of repeating decimals, I will limit the exploration to dividends equal to 1. In that case, which are the divisors that yield terminating decimals and which yield repeating decimals? And why?

C H A P T E R

# 8

# Highlights of related research

*by Sophia Cohen*

| SECTION 1 | Written number vs. spoken number |
| SECTION 2 | Seeing a ten as "one" |
| SECTION 3 | Invented procedures for adding and subtracting |
| SECTION 4 | Invented procedures for multiplying and dividing |
| SECTION 5 | Understanding decimal fractions |

U p to now, *Building a System of Tens* has focused on case materials written by teachers, relating episodes in their elementary and middle school classrooms. Through these cases, we have been able to look very closely at some of the complexities facing students as they build a conception of the base ten structure of our number system. In chapter 8, we shift our focus in two ways. First, we look at the story emerging from research on the development of these understandings, and we explore the connections between this research-based story and the classroom cases in the previous seven chapters. The case writers and the researchers share an important interest: carefully observing and coming to a better understanding of students' mathematical thinking. We bring together the research and the cases because both provide windows on students' development of very complex ideas.

The second shift in focus that we make in this chapter is from the particular to the general. Our picture is less fine-grained now, and we take this step back from the individual idea, or student, or classroom, to view a broader picture. Here we look at the whole set of issues students confront and work through as they come to understand the system-of-tens structure of our number system.

This essay examines five different themes, drawing on relevant mathematics, research, and cases from *Building a System of Tens*. First we consider the spoken and written systems for representing number, their similarities and differences, and the difficulties students face in learning about the written system. Second, we examine what is involved in understanding that a group of any size can itself be counted as a "one"; that, for instance, ten is simultaneously 1 ten and 10 ones. Third, we examine the issues that arise for students as they add and subtract multidigit numbers; fourth, we focus on issues related to multiplication and division. Finally, we take up decimal fractions and explore the ways students work to build understandings of these numbers, starting from their understandings of whole numbers and of common fractions. Together these five themes illustrate the issues students confront as they build more and more powerful understandings of the base ten number system.

SECTION 1

# Written number vs. spoken number

*Spoken and written number are different systems. They are related to each other in complex ways; building an understanding of each system and its relationship to the other involves substantial work.*

While we are all aware of both speaking and writing number, we do not often stop to consider the ways in which spoken and written number are similar to, or different from, one another. As it turns out, in English, the relationships are rather complicated. Children come to school relatively experienced with the spoken system and relatively inexperienced with the written system and with the similarities or differences between them. The spoken and written number systems have two very important similarities. First, both systems use successive powers of ten as the units. In other words, in both spoken and written number, we work with units of ones, tens, hundreds, thousands, and so forth. Second, both systems use ten different words or marks to represent the numbers 0 through 9, and then reuse these same words or marks to indicate how many of the larger units there are.

These similarities are so impressive that the differences may, at first, be difficult for adults to notice. But the differences are also impressive. The primary difference is that in the number system of spoken English, we explicitly name the value of the units (e.g., four *thousand* five *hundred* eighty-three).[1] In the written system, we rely on unnamed position, or place value, to convey their value (e.g., 4,583).

An experiment can illustrate the significance of this. Suppose that you write the words for a four-digit number on separate cards. On one card you write *four thousand,* on the next *five hundred,* on the next *eighty,* and on the last *three.* Now scramble and read these cards; *three five hundred four thousand eighty* is one possibility. Even scrambled, the number words still indicate the original quantity. They don't do it in the conventional way, but they are not ambiguous, nor has their meaning changed. Now suppose that instead of writing number words on these cards, you write the numerals for the same quantity. On the first card you write 4, on the next 5, on the next 8, and on the last 3. Now, when you scramble these, what happens? Or what if you maintain the order, but separate the numerals from one another? Your representation no longer maintains the original meaning. The meaning of the unit size in written number is conveyed only through the place or position in which the number is written. The unit value is not otherwise explicitly marked or named as it is in the spoken system.

---

[1] Note that while we name all units greater than or less than 1 (tens, hundreds, etc., as well as tenths, hundredths, etc.), units of size 1 are not named in spoken English.

The learner's job is even more difficult because, in English, the spoken number system for the numbers between 11 and 100 is irregular in many ways and does not consistently highlight the base ten structure of our number system (Fuson, 1990, 2003; Fuson, Wearne, et al., 1997; Miura & Okamoto, 2003). For example:

- English number words for two-digit numbers do not include the word *ten*. Instead we use *-teen* and *-ty*. Thus, not only do we *not* use the word *ten* itself, but we use two different variants of it.

- The placement of the ten in *-teen* words is the reverse of the placement of the ten in *-ty* words. So while we say "four*teen*," indicating first how many ones and then how many tens, we say "*forty*-four," indicating first how many tens and then how many ones.

- The words *eleven* and *twelve* don't mark tens at all.

- The words *thirteen* and *fifteen* do mark tens and ones, but alter the pronunciation of the three and five, making the *-teen* pattern (thirteen through nineteen) difficult to notice and use.

- A similar problem exists with the *-ty* words: *twenty*, *thirty*, and *fifty* alter the pronunciation of the two, three, and five on which they are based.

Karen Fuson (1990) found that, because of the differences between the spoken and written systems, three issues arise for children as they begin to map between spoken and written number. The cases in this casebook provide examples that parallel Fuson's findings.

The first issue emerges because in spoken number, we can omit a value term as we name some quantities and still be clear on the quantity; this is not paralleled in written number. In other words, we can say "six hundred two," but its written equivalent is not 62; in the written system where position or place marks unit size, we must write 602. We do not say "six hundred, zero tens, two" (although we can imagine such a system), presumably because the values of the units are named in the spoken system, and the "zero tens" isn't necessary.

In Muriel's case 8, second graders are thinking about questions related to this issue: what zero represents, and whether or not it represents the same thing in the numbers 07 and 70. These children seem to be thinking very seriously about the structure of our written number system, and they are beginning to grapple with the question of how and why zero of a given unit (ones, tens, hundreds) is represented.

A second difficulty that arises from the differences between spoken and written number could be viewed as the reverse of the first. The question here is whether each system tolerates more than nine of a given unit. For example, a child who is adding 58 and 37 might come to an answer of "eighty-fifteen" and get stuck at this point. In the spoken system, "eighty-fifteen" is a sensible, if not conventional, representation of the quantity that results from adding 58 and 37. However, neither 815 nor 8015 are the corresponding written number; in fact there is no way to write that number without symbols representing the implied operation of addition (80 + 15).

In Dawn's case 6, kindergartners are discussing how to write the number that follows 59. They debate whether it should be 510 ("fifty-ten" as Andrew says it) or 60. These children are working on, among other things, questions like those involved in the "eighty-fifteen" example. They are uncovering elements of the structure of our written number system.

A third difficulty stems from the fact that spoken number names the unit while written number does not. In spoken number, the values are named and follow one another, so we say, for example, "one hundred thirty-two." Written numbers, on the other hand, are embedded in one another; for the spoken "one hundred thirty-two," we write 132. It is not conventional to write 100302 for this quantity, although we see many children inventing this notation (Fuson, Wearne, et al., 1997; Seron, Deloche, & Noel, 1992; Seron & Fayol, 1994).

In the cases in chapter 2, we see children struggling with this issue, both in questions of how to write numbers and how to interpret them. In Danielle's case 7, children wonder whether one hundred ninety-five is written 195 or 1095 or 10095; in Muriel's case 8, a second grader argues that one hundred twenty-five cannot be correctly written as 100205. In Donna's case 9, the children have not yet unpacked the embedded numbers in the written form. For instance, we encounter her second-grade students as they are just coming to see that 38 is comprised of 3 tens (or "thir-ty") and 8 ones.

And with larger numbers, involving more places, there are more of these compositions to understand. For example, the written number 132 can be understood as 1 hundred + 3 tens + 2 ones; but it can also be seen as 13 tens + 2 ones, or as 132 ones, or as 1 hundred + 32 ones. As the cases make clear, these equivalencies are not at all trivial or obvious, and in the next section we'll look more at how this knowledge develops. For now, as we focus on the relationship between spoken and written number, we note that when languages offer clear labels for unit, this feature may be quite helpful to children as they first learn about base ten numbers.[2] As students come to understand more about the base ten structure of our number system, however, written number provides a representation that enables them to imagine different ways of breaking apart the same written form. Spoken English allows this to some extent; for 1,100, we say both *eleven hundred* and *one thousand one hundred*. However, we don't conventionally refer to the quantity 20,000 as *two hundred hundreds* or *two thousand tens*. In written form, and in computation, such flexibility in conceptualizing these numbers is both possible and a strength.

[2] The Chinese, Japanese, and Korean languages all clearly and regularly mark the tens structure of two-digit numbers; they name 11, 12 , and 13 *ten-one*, *ten-two*, and *ten-three*, and name 21, 31, and 41 *two-ten-one*, *three-ten-one*, and *four-ten-one*. Young children who speak these languages differ from those who speak English and other European languages in how they make use of blocks to represent a quantity such as 42. Miura and Okamoto (2003) studied Chinese, Japanese, and Korean children as well as American, Swedish, and French children early in grade 1. This was before any of the children had received any school instruction in the tens structure of number or in base ten blocks. All children were introduced to base ten blocks and were asked to use the blocks to show different quantities, such as 42. The 6-year-old European language speakers were most likely to represent the quantity using 42 unit blocks. Their Asian language speaking counterparts were significantly more likely to represent 42 as 4 tens and 2 ones. Miura and Okamoto interpret their findings as suggesting that the structure of the number names in Asian languages offers a better tool to children as they work to understand the tens structure of our number system. Exactly what meaning these block constructions have is not clear from the authors' report. For example, it is difficult to tell whether the Asian children's tens and ones constructions are representing only the number words of their language, or whether they also reflect a deeper understanding of the quantitative relationship between tens and ones. Further, other researchers (Towse & Saxton, 1998) argue that language may not have such a strong effect, finding that small changes in the questions asked eliminate the differences that Miura and Okamoto found.

Building a System of Tens

Most of the research on the relationship between spoken and written number has focused on young children learning about numbers up to 100. Skwarchuk and Anglin (2002), however, studied children's naming of written numbers up to one trillion (1,000,000,000,000—a number we so rarely see written in this form). They asked students in grades 1, 3, 5, and 7 to name and to count on from written numbers sampled across the range between 10 and one trillion. Their results point to a long learning trajectory. For example, even though some first-grade children knew all of the basic number words up to 100 (names for all of the single digit, teen, and decade numbers) and could use these to generate some of the number names to 100, they weren't doing so consistently for all numbers up to 100. Third-grade children show a similar pattern (correctly naming some, but not others) in their naming of numbers in the low thousands. In contrast, most of the fifth-grade and seventh-grade students who could correctly name one number of a certain size (e.g., hundred millions or ten billions) were always correct at that level. It seems that these older students have a kind of knowledge of the rules for producing number names that younger children are still developing.

Skwarchuk and Anglin also looked carefully at the third-grade students' responses, finding that their naming and counting were considerably better for numbers in the low thousands than they were for numbers in the tens of thousands, and that they had the most difficulty with numbers in the hundreds of thousands. This result is not surprising. But the authors note that in the thousands, students first encounter the situation that with an increase in the number of digits, a new basic naming word is not introduced. Two-digit numbers they have learned to label with -*teen* and -*ty*, three-digit numbers with *hundred*, four-digit numbers with *thousand*. As students begin to label numbers with five and more digits, there is a new naming pattern to understand, one that uses the names of numbers in the tens and hundreds in combination with the word *thousands*. Once students have come to understand this naming pattern, it will help them to generate the names of numbers in the millions, billions, trillions, and so on.

Finally, in Skwarchuk and Anglin's study, it was generally not until fifth-grade that students were able to continue a counting sequence into the millions, and not until seventh-grade that they did so into the billions. Susie's case 11 is consistent with this. Here Trinia, a sixth-grade student, is working to learn the place-name associations for numbers in the billions and trillions. Even though these older students come to this task with considerable knowledge of the spoken and written number systems for smaller numbers, and perhaps even the relative sizes represented by the larger written numbers (i.e., that 1,000,000 is less than 1,000,000,000), there continues to be more for them to learn about the relationship between number names and written numbers.

Students are faced with an enormous amount of work to sort through the ways we write and speak about number and how these two systems relate to one another. Beyond this, of course, we want students to connect these symbols to some sense of the quantities they represent. We turn to these issues next.

S E C T I O N   2

# Seeing a ten as "one"

*Being able to label the tens place and the ones place, or even being able to count by tens, does not necessarily signal an understanding that 1 ten is simultaneously 10 ones. Becoming mindful of this relationship between tens and ones, or staying mindful of it, is neither simple nor trivial.*

Mommy, if you are 40, then 30 years ago you had to be 1. Oh, wait! I was forgetting about 31, 32, 33, 34, . . .

Nina (Grade 2, October)

In this short quote, we see one moment of a child's struggle to keep track of a ten as both 1 ten and 10 ones. We see a very similar struggle played out in Lucy's case 4, in which third grader Sarah is confused about how many black cubes (representing ones) to move over to the yellows (representing tens): If she is representing the number 10, should she move ten cubes or should she move one? These children are showing us the

Building a System of Tens

complexity involved in building a notion of 10 as a unit and integrating this unit of 10 with their long-held notion of 1 as a unit. This conceptual structure—the structure at the very heart of our base ten number system—is far from obvious.

While children may fairly readily come to label the left digit of a two-digit written number as the *tens* and the right digit as the *ones*, this knowledge of written number names does not necessarily signal an understanding of a "ten" as being 10 ones and related either to the ones or to the whole number in a quantitative way. Both our cases and a long history of more formal research suggest that working out this aspect of number is a protracted process (e.g., Beishuizen, 1993; Cobb, 1995; Cobb & Wheatley, 1988; Fuson, 1990; Fuson, Wearne, et al., 1997; Opfer & Siegler, 2007; Ross, 1989; Steffe, 1988; Steffe, Cobb, & Von Glasersfeld, 1988; Varelas & Becker, 1997).

A careful look at the way that multidigit written numbers represent quantities can help us to understand some of the complexity that students are sorting through. In a place value system, one symbol (the digits 0, 1, 2, 3, … 9) can have many meanings. The same written digit, 2 for example, can refer to 2, 20, 200, and so on, depending on the place it occupies. That each symbol can have many meanings reflects the implied multiplication of the place value system. And in order to understand these numbers, we must keep track of both the *number of groups* and the *number in each group*. The written digit represents the number of groups, while the place—without explicitly labeling it—represents the size of that group (1, 10, 100, etc.). So, for example, 2 in the ones place represents 2(1), 2 in the tens place represents 2(10), 2 in the hundreds place represents 2(100), and so on. Further, in order to fully understand a number written in the place value system, we must come to see its value as composed by both multiplication and addition. We multiply to determine the value within a place, while across places we sum these values. The whole quantity represented by written number relies on both multiplication and addition: 37, for example, represents the quantity $(3 \times 10) + (7 \times 1)$.

A small portion of a much larger experiment conducted by Maria Varelas and Joe Becker (1997) clearly exposes children's initial understandings of two-digit number as based on units of a value of 1, and their difficulty in imposing a tens and ones structure on these same quantities. Varelas and Becker met individually with 144 children in grades 2 through 4. They showed each child the written number 23. After

the child read the number aloud, the researcher poured 23 beans from
a bag into a cup, calling the child's attention to the match between the
written number and the number of beans that she was giving the child.
Then, separately for each digit of the written number and beginning with
the 3 in the ones place, the researcher pointed to that digit and asked the
child "to put the right amount of the 23 beans for this part" into an empty
cup placed near the written digit.

If a child answered correctly for both digits—putting 20 beans in the
cup near the tens place and 3 beans in the cup near the ones place—the
researcher probed a little further. Removing the correct 20 beans from
the cup for the value of the tens digit, the researcher put in only 2 beans,
saying "Another child did this. Is that a good way of doing it?" and
asking the child to explain why or why not.

If a child originally put an incorrect number of beans in either cup,
the researcher offered a hint. Asking the child to read the number again,
the researcher lifted up the two cups together (the cup near the ones digit
and the cup near the tens digit) and asked the child how many beans
there were altogether in the two cups.

Varelas and Becker noticed two things in children's answers. First,
only about one third of the children interpreted the digit in the tens
place as referring to the quantity 20.[3] Even counting as correct those
responses that were prompted by the hint, two thirds of the children
in this study made errors. And nearly all of the errors involved placing
a number of beans corresponding to the face value (2) rather than the
complete value—2(10), or 20—for the digit in the tens place. The fact that
this is a common error, along with the fact that none of the 144 children
in the study explained this allotment of beans—either spontaneously or
when probed by the researcher's question—by saying that the 2 beans
in one cup was to indicate 2 *tens*, suggests that these children are not

[3] The results reported here are from the use of the bean task as a pre-test by
  Varelas and Becker. The full study goes on to explore the effects of different
  kinds of learning experiences on this task and others.
[4] This first finding from Varelas and Becker is not particular to their wording,
  materials, or children. Other researchers find similar things using other procedures and materials (e.g., Kamii, 1989; Ross, 1989).

interpreting the separate digits of this multidigit number as referring to different kinds of units.[4]

Second, fewer than half the children appeared to interpret the two digits of the written number as referring to two quantities that summed to form a third quantity, represented by the entire written number. For evidence of this kind of thinking, Varelas and Becker looked at how children came to their correct answers in the bean task. Specifically, they noticed that children used one of two strategies for putting beans in the cup corresponding to the value of the tens digit: counting or dumping. Even as the researchers continued their study and more children came to correctly answer some version of the bean task, counting was the strategy that children most often used to put the correct number of beans in this second cup. Dumping was less common. Although children who counted to arrive at their answers might or might not understand the implied addition in a multidigit number's representation of quantity (e.g., 20 + 3 = 23), it seemed likely to Varelas and Becker that when children dump the remaining beans they are, in effect, saying that after placing the number of beans indicated by the digit in the ones place, all the rest—whatever that number is—constitute the quantity represented by the digit in the tens place, and thus they do understand the implied addition. Indeed, this interpretation was born out in a follow-up study. The children who dumped beans in the original study also participated in the new study; it was exactly like the first, except that instead of starting with a known number of beans (23), children were told, "Now I'm going to give you a cup of beans. I don't know how many beans there are." In this situation, in which the beans may or may not be the quantity represented by the written number, children counted rather than dumped, suggesting that their choice of dumping in the first study reflected their recognition that the quantity referred to by a two-digit number is the sum of the complete value of each digit.

What we see overall in the Varelas and Becker bean task (and other related studies, e.g., Kamii, 1989; Ross, 1989) is that at least across the early elementary grades, children are still working hard to develop an understanding of the tens structure of number and its representation in written form.

An influential paper published in 1997 by a collaborative group of researchers from four different projects describes the different understandings of multidigit numbers that students build as they gain experience (Fuson, Wearne, et al., 1997). These researchers described the ways of thinking about two-digit numbers that they found to be common to students across all of their projects. Altogether, Fuson and colleagues describe six different conceptions or ways of thinking about these numbers; five are correct conceptions and one is incorrect. The authors note that the different conceptions they describe do not constitute stages in any strict sense. In their observations, students tended to build new conceptual structures alongside old ones, adding new to old, rather than replacing one with the other. Thus, for any given student, more than one of these ways of thinking about numbers between 11 and 100 may be in play; perhaps the student is thinking of some numbers one way and others in other ways, or thinking about some situations differently from others. While this variety of conceptualizations precludes any simple description of students' understanding, the variety obtained by adding new conceptual structures to old ones (rather than replacing one with another) eventually supports a flexibility with multidigit numbers that is a hallmark of understanding the base ten system.

The first conceptual structure that these researchers propose is the *unitary multidigit conception*. This unitary conception grows from children's understanding of single-digit numbers. A child operating with a unitary conception does not differentiate a quantity into groupings, but rather treats the number in its entirety as the name for the quantity in its entirety.

In what may be the next conception to develop (Fuson, Smith, & LoCicero, 1997), children begin to separate out the tens portion of the number from the ones portion. Fuson and colleagues call this the *decade and ones conception*. Thinking in this way, a child hearing or counting the number words *forty-three* would hear in this separately the decade quantity label (*forty*) and the ones label (*three*) and relate them to the quantities 40 and 3. This conception is an advance over the unitary conception, but children are still not thinking of quantities (even the decade quantity, e.g., 40) as further broken down into groups. The authors note that this decades and ones conception is seen at the same time that many children are, for example, writing 403 for the number forty-three. Danielle's case 7 is a good illustration of this way of thinking. While these first-grade children are not thinking about a two-digit number, but about the three-digit number 195 (or 1095, or 10095), they articulate the same kind of reasoning.

285

290

295

300

305

310

315

320

Building a System of Tens

The next three conceptions that Fuson and colleagues describe, unlike these first ones, involve explicit groupings of ten. The authors note that for these conceptions, their relative strength, their order, and even their existence depends in large measure on a child's instructional environment (Fuson, Wearne, et al., 1997; Fuson, Smith, & LoCicero, 1997). One of these more explicit tens structures is the *sequence-tens and ones conception*, in which children who have had experience counting by tens now conceive of the decade portion of a quantity as a sequence of tens. Here, a child would count out 43 cups by seeing the tens in the quantity and counting "ten, twenty, thirty, forty, forty-one, forty-two, forty-three." The child does not see this 10, 20, 30, 40 count as 4 tens (at least initially and within this conception), but once grouped in sequence-tens in this way, the number of tens could be counted.

It is largely this kind of knowledge that distinguishes the next conception, the *separate-tens and ones conception*, from the sequence-tens conception. With the separate-tens and ones conception, children conceive of two different kinds of units, tens and ones, and count each separately. So with our cups example, this conception allows a count of 1, 2, 3, 4 tens and 1, 2, 3 ones. Children who understand two-digit number and quantity in this way understand that each of the tens is composed of 10 ones; they can choose to break down a ten into its component ones (e.g., 4 tens into 3 tens + 10 ones) if that is useful in a particular problem context. Donna's second graders in case 9, who group a certain quantity of beans in different ways (by 7s, by 10s, by 3s, etc.), record whole groups and leftovers, and discover what they call the "tens trick," are building this separate-tens and ones conception.

The last correct conceptual structure that Fuson and colleagues describe is a combination of the separate-tens and ones and the sequence-tens and ones conceptions. This *integrated sequence-separate tens conception* is at play when children know immediately that, for example, 40 has 4 tens. Without this integration, and working from the sequence conception, the child must count by tens to 40, keeping track of the number of times ten was counted. Working from the separate-tens conception, the child must count out 4 tens to arrive at 40. With the two conceptions integrated, however, children can move back and forth flexibly and rapidly between conceptions.

Finally, this group of researchers describes one incorrect way of thinking about multidigit numbers. With this conception, the concatenated *single-digit conception*, children treat written multidigit

numbers as if each digit refers to the same quantity it would refer to
as a single digit. Fuson and colleagues saw this way of thinking about
multidigit numbers even in some children who also had one of the
adequate conceptions. It is often seen when addition or subtraction
problems are presented vertically. Yet this is the same error that children
made in the Varelas and Becker bean task where they were not being
asked to add two multidigit numbers, but just to indicate the quantity
represented by each digit.

While Fuson and colleagues describe these six different conceptions
of multidigit number in most detail for two-digit numbers, they find that
the same conceptual structures are later extended to three- and four-digit
numbers.

As researchers make progress in describing how young students
develop understanding of the tens structure of our number system,
three points seem clear. First, people think about multidigit numbers
and quantities in many different ways. Second, many different ways
of thinking about these numbers coexist within any given person.
Third, developments in understanding smaller multidigit numbers
and quantities are followed at a later time by parallel developments in
understanding larger multidigit numbers and quantities (Booth & Siegler,
2006; Fuson, Wearne, et al., 1997; Opfer & Siegler, 2007).

So far the research we have looked at focuses on the child's sense
of the structure of a certain quantity. Other researchers, however, have
focused on children's sense of the relative positions or magnitudes of
different numbers (Booth & Siegler, 2006; Opfer & Siegler, 2007; Siegler
& Opfer, 2003; Siegler & Booth, 2005). These researchers have studied
children's estimates of the size of numbers and have systematically
looked at children's placements of numbers on number lines that are
labeled only with two anchor points, such as 0 near one end and 100
near the other. These researchers find that children (and adults) have
two general representations or models of magnitude: one linear and the
other nonlinear. The linear model matches our formal number system:
a distance of 1 is always the same size whether we are considering
the distance between 0 and 1 or between 1,000,000 and 1,000,001. The
nonlinear model has a different logic. The size of numbers increases more
rapidly among smaller numbers than it does among larger numbers.
And this makes sense in many situations. For example, we might care
more about the difference between having two cookies and having three
of them, than we do about the difference between having 100 cookies

or 101. Similarly, if our savings go from $1 to $100, this increase is more important than a similar increase from $1,000,001 to $1,000,100.

Siegler and his colleagues have found that between kindergarten and second grade, children's placement of numbers on a 0 to 100 number line shifts from the incorrect nonlinear model to a correct linear placement of numbers along the line (Siegler & Booth, 2004). Similarly, between second and sixth grade, the same shift is seen for placing numbers on a 0 to 1,000 number line (Siegler & Opfer, 2003). Siegler and Opfer (2003) also found that individual children simultaneously have and use both models. Almost half the second graders placed numbers on a 0 to 100 number line in a linear way, while they placed numbers on a 0 to 1,000 number line in a nonlinear way. Indeed, we see evidence of this in Leslie's case 10, both from Olivia, who begins by placing 500 at the middle of the number line labeled from 0 to 10,000, and from Chris, whose 0 to 10,000 number line makes the intervals of 100 between the numbers 0 and 1,000 equal to the intervals of 1,000 between the numbers 1,000 and 10,000.

In Robert Siegler and colleagues' work on this topic, as with the Fuson, Wearne, et al. research, we see evidence of more than one way of understanding the relative sizes of multidigit numbers. We again see that the different ways of thinking about these numbers coexist in the same child. And we again see that the same developmental progression evidenced with smaller numbers is retraced later as children come to know larger numbers better.

SECTION 3

# Invented procedures for adding and subtracting

*As children gain facility in breaking apart and recombining numbers, they invent multidigit addition and subtraction procedures. These can be the starting places for deeper understanding of the tens structure itself and how it behaves in computation.*

It is an enormous leap from operating with units of one to multidigit computational procedures that use units of tens, hundreds, thousands, and so forth, as well as units of one. To work with units of different values, we must sort out the complicated ways that each is related to the others. The number 107, for example, can be thought of as 1 hundred + 0 tens + 7 ones, or as 10 tens + 7 ones, or as 107 ones; and if we now want to add 38, which is to say 3 tens + 8 ones or 38 ones, to our initial 107, there are several possibilities. We might think about this problem entirely in terms of ones (as we usually would for a problem such as 4 + 2). We could add 107 ones to 38 ones, yielding 145 ones, an answer we could arrive at by counting. Alternatively, we might think about the numbers involved in this problem as each being composed of a certain number of units of different values. Perhaps we set aside the 1 hundred of 107, and then add on 3 tens of 38, and next the 8 ones and the 7 ones. Or, we might think of the 100 as 10 tens, add these to the 3 tens from 38 to find 13 tens, to which we would still need to add the 8 ones and the 7 ones in some way. When it comes to the 7 + 8 portion of this problem, there are also many possibilities. We might add 7 ones to the 8 ones as a single quantity that yields 15 ones; or we might add in parts, for instance, taking 2 ones (from the 7) to add to the 8 ones, thus making a fourteenth ten and 5 more ones.

Any solution that makes use of units other than one either requires some knowledge of the effects of adding units of different values, or it requires a method for modeling and investigating these. In order to combine the 13 tens and 15 ones from our example, and to name this number in a conventional way, a person needs to know the precise quantitative relationships between ones and tens and between tens and hundreds. Similar knowledge is necessary for a multiunit solution to a subtraction problem such as 107 − 38 (although, as we will see later, the subtraction situation poses further difficulties). And this is all for a problem involving numbers of just two or three digits. With larger numbers (in the thousands, millions, etc.) or smaller numbers (decimals) come more places, more units of different sizes, and more quantitative relationships to work out.

Because of the issues surrounding units and their relationships to one another that arise during computation, multidigit addition and subtraction can be a vehicle for learning about the meanings that underlie our place value system. Indeed, children often use adequate methods for multidigit addition and subtraction of two- and three-digit numbers *before* they demonstrate fundamental understanding of place value (Fuson, Wearne, et al. 1997; Varelas & Becker, 1997; Jacobs, 2002; Carpenter et al., 1998), and their knowledge of the tens structure grows through in-depth exploration of computation strategies (Jacobs, 2002; Carpenter et al., 1996; Carpenter et al., 1998; Cobb, 1995; Cobb & Wheatley, 1988; Fuson, 1990; Ross, 1989; Wood, 1996). How does this happen?

Without explicit instruction, children devise computational procedures that directly model the actions and relations of a word problem. To develop these procedures, children draw on their understanding of counting and of the kinds of change (adding some or taking some away) that affect quantity, that is, their knowledge about making more or making less. Initially, children's strategies are based in a system of ones (counting all, counting on, and counting back). Eventually, children develop strategies for other-sized groups, including the very powerful use of ones, tens, hundreds, and so forth (Carpenter et al., 1996; Carpenter et al., 1998; Fuson, Wearne, et al., 1997; Resnick, 1992; Resnick, Lesgold, & Bill, 1990; Madell, 1985).

We see examples of both ones-based and tens-based strategies in Lynn's case 12. Lynn describes second graders solving a word problem in which teachers at recess see 38 children around the climbing structure and 25 children playing freeze tag. The problem asks how many children the teachers see. Several children counted by ones to solve this problem. Two children did as follows: They made two Unifix cube collections, one of 38 and one of 25, counting out the cubes one by one. Next, they counted both sets together, starting at one, until all cubes were counted. This contrasts with the solutions of several other children in the same class who worked more abstractly with number rather than physical models and who combined units separately (first tens, then ones), generating solutions such as this one: $30 + 20 = 50$, $8 + 5 = 13$, $50 + 13 = 63$. Like many children (and unlike the conventional written procedures), these students chose to operate with the larger numbers (in this case, tens) first (Madell, 1985; Kamii, 1989; Kamii, Lewis, & Livingston, 1993; Kilpatrick, Swafford, & Findell, 2001).

While this latter-style solution certainly demonstrates some ability to decompose and recombine numbers using groups of tens and ones, we are not able to tell from this example whether any of these students understand 30 + 20 = 50 to be equivalent to 3 tens + 2 tens = 5 tens, and therefore to be both similar to, and different from, 3 ones + 2 ones = 5 ones. Certainly the students solving this problem by counting out cubes one by one are not looking at the numbers this way.

A study conducted by Thomas Carpenter, Megan Franke, Victoria Jacobs, Elizabeth Fennema, and Susan Empson (1998) sheds some light on how this knowledge develops. These researchers conducted a three-year study of the development of multidigit number concepts and operations, interviewing 82 children in first grade through third grade, five times over the three years. The teachers whose students participated in this study were part of a three-year professional development program designed to help teachers to understand and build on children's mathematical ideas, but the program did not involve any specific classroom curriculum materials or guidelines.

Carpenter and colleagues offer a taxonomy of the strategies for multidigit addition and subtraction that they saw among the children they studied.[5] The strategies they describe begin with children's direct modeling of problems with physical materials, first by ones (as we saw the students doing with Unifix cubes in the example from Lynn's case 12), and then modeling with various materials representing tens.[6]

An example from an earlier study by Carpenter, Fennema, and Franke (1996) offers an illustration of a student's use of physical materials to model the tens structure of numbers in a mutidigit addition situation. This is a particularly nice example, because in it we also see the student's use of these physical models to build a purely numeric method of adding these numbers (McClain, Cobb, and Bowers, 1998, also describe this same kind of progression.)

---

[5] The strategies described by Carpenter and colleagues (1998) largely correspond to a similar taxonomy described by Fuson, Wearne, et al. (1997) and to others reviewed by Verschaffel, Greer, and DeCorte (2007).

[6] Physical models might be actual objects, as in these examples with interlocking cubes. They might also be drawings or diagrams created by a child.

Carpenter and colleagues provide the following example from a third-grade class that has been asked to solve a word problem involving the sum 54 + 48:

Ms. G:    Now everyone go over to Ellen's desk.

Ellen:    They don't need to go to my desk. I can tell them right here.

Ms. G:    But I want them to go to your desk; I want them to see exactly what you showed me, and then you can tell me how you could do it without us having to go to your desk.

[*The children move around Ellen's desk.*]

Ellen:    [*Makes 54 and 48 with tens and ones blocks (5 tens blocks and 4 ones blocks and separately 4 tens blocks and 8 ones blocks)*]. I know this was 54, so I went 64, 74, 84, 94 [*Ellen moves one ten block for each count. Then she counts the single cubes, moving a cube with each count.*] 95, 96, . . . 102 . . .

Ms. G:    OK, now you told me that you could do this without us moving to your desk. How would you have done that?

Ellen:    OK, I just put 54 in my head, and then I go 48 more. I go 54 [*slight pause*], 64, 74, 84, 94 [*She puts up a finger with each count to keep track of the tens. At this point she has 4 fingers up. She puts down her fingers and puts them up again with each count as she continues counting by ones.*] 95, 96, 97, . . . 102. (pp. 3–4)

Ellen first solves this problem with blocks. She begins with the physical materials, representing tens and ones separately to support her count of "64, 74, 84, 94, 95, 96, 97, ... 102." However, once given the opportunity to share her solution, she is eager to speak about it without blocks and seems to have already moved to an understanding that she can communicate without directly manipulating physical objects.

From many examples similar to this sequence, Carpenter et a1. (1996) propose that

the manipulations of the blocks become objects of reflection. At some point the numbers involved in counting the blocks also become objects of reflection so that students can operate on the numbers independently of the blocks. A key factor

in this process is the continuing discussion of alternative
strategies. Students regularly are called upon to articulate
their solutions, to describe in words what they have done
with the blocks. In order to be able to describe their strategies,
they need to reflect upon them, to decide how to report
them verbally. Initially the descriptions are of procedures
that have already been carried out. Eventually the words
that students use to describe their manipulations of blocks
become the solutions themselves. Thus, the verbal description
of modeling strategies provides a basis for connecting
manipulations of tens blocks and invented algorithms using
numbers only. The students do not imitate a strategy that
they do not understand; they abstract the physical modeling
procedures when they are comfortable doing so. (pp. 12–13)

Carpenter and colleagues are ascribing importance to a child's
understanding of the relationship between the mathematical problem
and the physical objects, blocks in this case, and then again a child's
understanding of the relationship between the physical objects and the
numbers as each are operated on. The emphasis here is on the child's
understanding, the meaning that a child makes. There is no particular
meaning that a given set of materials is expected to have for all children,
or for one child at all times; rather, materials are used by children to sort
out their current understandings and to build new ones.

As the example of Ellen illustrates, children use their work with
physical models of multidigit addition to invent methods of computation
that do not rely on physical materials, but are carried out on the numbers
themselves. Children's invented numerical strategies for addition are of
three general kinds (Carpenter et al., 1998; Fuson, Wearne, et al., 1997;
Verschaffel, Greer, & DeCorte, 2007). Researchers differ in the details
of what they call the different methods or even exactly how many
categories of strategies they describe, but there is broad agreement that
the following kinds of invented strategies are common among children
(Verschaffel et al., 2007): sequential strategies, combining-units-separately
strategies, and compensating strategies, as well as mixtures of these.

If we take the problem 56 + 37 as an example, a *sequential strategy*
involves beginning with one quantity, say 56, and keeping a running
total of the result while adding 37, sometimes in convenient parts. Such

560

565

570

575

580

585

590

a strategy might yield the following kind of reasoning: 56 + 30 = 86; 86 + 4 = 90; 90 + 3 = 93. A *combining-units-separately* strategy treats the different units (in this example, tens and ones) separately from each other and then combines them. Such a strategy might yield the following solution: 50 + 30 = 80; 6 + 7 = 13; 80 + 13 = 93. The tens-based solutions from the playground problem in Lynn's case 12 are of this kind. In the third general kind of strategy, a *compensating* strategy, children adjust the numbers as needed to simplify the calculations. This kind of strategy might yield the following reasoning: 56 + 37 is like 60 + 33, so the sum is 93. Finally, some solutions combine these different strategies (Fuson, Wearne, et al., 1997; Verschaffel et al., 2007).

These same kinds of methods are seen in the computational procedures that children invent for subtraction, but with subtraction these strategies are more difficult to implement (Carpenter et al., 1998). Children working on multiunit solutions to subtraction problems face a complicated set of issues that are not present with addition problems. With an addition problem, all quantities, no matter how we have broken them apart, are eventually recombined by addition to find the sum. Parts from the different addends can be rearranged in whatever way makes the calculations more convenient. With subtraction, however, as we break apart numbers for easier handling, we must now keep straight which numbers belong to the quantity that is being subtracted, and which belong to the quantity from which we are subtracting. So, for example, if the problem is 37 − 19, any tens-based solution strategy will lead us immediately to issues about how to treat the 7 and the 9.

In Lynn's case 13, "Subtraction and Invented Algorithms," Fiona's work shows us some of the difficulties in keeping track that arise with subtraction; and perhaps these difficulties make the tens-and-ones partitioning of the numbers in the problem less straightforward than it might be for an addition problem using similar numbers. Fiona was working on a word problem, which she represented as 37 − 19. She broke the problem down making use of tens. She first dealt with 30 − 10, then subtracted 9 more (20 − 9 = 11), and then wondered what she needed to do with the 7 that she had dropped from the initial 37. For Fiona, her teacher's question about whether the pigeons stayed or left helped her to sort out what she wanted to do with the 7, and she added it (11 + 7 = 18). Perhaps, though we don't know from a single case, even children who work relatively abstractly and independently of the problem context for addition still rely on a more concrete representation when faced with the complexities of subtraction.

To recap Fiona's solution to this problem, she begins with the tens, subtracting the 10 in 19 from the 30 in 37: $30 - 10 = 20$. She then chooses to subtract the 9 ones of 19 from the 2 tens she has left. The question that she then faces is what operation to perform on the 7 ones that remain to be figured into her calculations. Other solutions highlight other issues.

One step in a solution that many children try is to find the difference between the larger and the smaller number of ones. Such a solution stays closer to the combining-units-separately strategy, as it can be used in addition situations or in subtraction that doesn't involve regrouping. The child operates first on one kind of unit, then on the other, and then combines these results. Thus, in the $37 - 19$ example, when turning to the ones some children try $9 - 7$ (Kamii, 1989; Wood, 1996). If the problem were an addition problem involving the same quantities ($37 + 19$), this strategy would not lead us into such complex terrain. We could add $7 + 9$ or $9 + 7$ to the 3 tens + 1 ten. We would still need to know how the resulting 16 could be combined with the 40, but whether we found it easier to add 7 to 9 or vice versa would not have much impact on the complexity of our work with tens.

This is not so with subtraction. With subtraction, if we decide to deal with the 7 and the 9 by subtracting 7 from 9 ($9 - 7 = 2$), we are choosing a very complicated solution strategy. In what way can $9 - 7$ be a step in an accurate solution to $37 - 19$? Subtracting 7 from 9 gives us information about exactly how many ones we need to take from one of the tens of 37. We don't need the whole 10, we need only whatever we can't get from the 7 ones. We need 2 more. So, $30 - 10 = 20$, $9 - 7 = 2$; we still need to subtract 2 ones from the 2 tens. However, in order to calculate the result of $20 - 2$, we must either think about the 20 as 20 ones or as 1 ten + 10 ones; in either case, subtracting 2 ones leaves us with 18.

Students in Emily's case 2 examine a solution to the problem $52 - 28$ that relies on these mathematical ideas. One child, Ivan, says, "You take the 20 away from the 50 and get 30. Then you take 8 away from 2, which is -6. Then you take 6 away from 30 and you get 24." Ivan hasn't yet explained why this procedure is a valid and accurate one, but in laying out this solution for consideration, he places himself and his fellow students squarely in front of some important mathematical ideas.

Building a System of Tens

We see these complexities of subtraction reflected in the pattern of
findings from the study conducted by Carpenter and colleagues (1998;
Jacobs, 2002). These researchers found that 33 percent of the 82 children
they studied (from first through third grade) had invented procedures
for both addition and subtraction before (or beginning at the same time
as) they began to use the U.S. standard algorithms for multidigit addition
and subtraction. Interestingly, however, even more of the children they
studied (40 percent) had invented procedures for multidigit *addition* prior
to using a standard algorithm for multidigit addition, but were *not* using
invented (numerical) procedures for *subtraction* prior to the classroom
introduction of a standard algorithm for multidigit subtraction. Due
to the complexity of subtraction, children seem to develop invented
multidigit procedures for this operation later than for addition.

Carpenter and colleagues were interested in whether there were
important learning consequences of children first working in their own
invented procedures before working to understand the U.S. standard
algorithms. To address this question, they looked at the knowledge
of base ten number concepts among the children who had invented
procedures (for either or both operations) before learning a standard
algorithm for that operation, and compared that with the base ten
knowledge of children who did *not* use invented procedures for
multidigit addition or subtraction before learning a standard algorithm.
Base ten knowledge was measured by five tasks, including one very
similar to the Varelas and Becker bean task described in the previous
section. The children who developed and worked with their own
procedures for addition or subtraction of multidigit numbers before
learning and working with standard algorithms showed stronger
knowledge of base ten number concepts than did those who did not
first work with invented procedures. While some of the difference in
knowledge preceded (and was a likely contributor to) the children's
invented procedures, this is not the whole story. Carpenter and his
colleagues also found that understanding of the place value system
was not necessary for children to begin inventing procedures for
multidigit addition and subtraction. Fully 28 percent of the children
in the study used invented procedures before showing a fundamental

670

675

680

685

690

695

700

grasp of the place value system (Carpenter et al., 1998; Jacobs, 2002). 705
Yet at a later time, after having used these invented procedures, the
children's understanding of the tens structure of our number system was
measurably better than those who had not yet worked with invented
procedures.

Thus Carpenter and his colleagues found that this process, beginning 710
with children's use of physical models for computation and classroom
discussion of these physical models, helps children not only begin to use
groupings of ten in invented computation procedures, but also come to
deeper understandings of how the units of different sizes (ones, tens,
hundreds, and so on) are related to one another and how the operations 715
of addition and subtraction might affect them.

Sarah, the third-grade student in Lucy's case 4, provides a wonderful
example of a child gaining new insights about tens and ones in this way.
We are told that Sarah is able to use the conventional algorithm and can
accurately solve two-digit addition problems in other ways as well. As 720
she tries to model the conventional algorithm with Unifix cubes, she
finds that she has more to understand about carrying the 1. She works
at understanding why she arrives at one answer with her block method,
in which she moves a stack of 1 ten over to the tens and then counts
them as 10 tens, and a different answer with the algorithm, in which the 725
1 represents a single unit of ten. As a result of this work, she comes to
understand something new about the relationship between tens and ones
and about the meanings of the places in written number. As Sarah says,
"If I put 10 of these up here [*pointing to the 10 black cubes attached above the
yellow*] it equals 1, not just 10." Her use of *just* is interesting. Since 10 is 730
a larger number than 1, she can't mean "a number as small as ... ," as a
child might mean by saying, "I have 5 marbles, not just 2." It seems that
she has discovered that "ten" can be 1 ten; it isn't "just" 10 ones. This
was new to her, and difficult to work out, despite the fact that she was
quite able to use the conventional algorithm to calculate the answer. Her 735
work to critically examine the reasons that different solution strategies
resulted in different answers provided her with a deeper knowledge of
the system of tens.

While most of the research has focused on children's work with two-
and three-digit numbers, we can see from both the cases and the previous 740
section of this essay that children meet similar issues as they work with
larger numbers. Indeed, in Olive's case 5, we see sixth-grade students
working out the relationships among units as they model solutions to

the problem 10,000 − 485. We hear one student, Emily, ask (referring to the large hundreds grid): "Doesn't it take 100 of these to make 10,000?" She then reasons: "It has to be, because 10 isn't enough, it's only 1,000. We need stacks of 10 [hundreds] for each thousand, so we'll need 10 of them." Even after children work out some understanding of the relationship between tens and ones, they still need to learn that, in our number system, ten-for-one and one-for-ten trades can be made at each pair of neighboring places. For each new place, children need to come to understand the value of that place in relation to the other places. Multidigit addition and subtraction provide a context in which this can happen.

S E C T I O N   4

# Invented procedures for multiplying and dividing

*Breaking apart numbers by tens is an important strategy in multidigit multiplication and division. But for these operations, this decomposition by tens must be carried out in a way that is consistent with the distributive property. In representing their solutions, children have opportunities to make discoveries about the distributive property and how it applies in multiplication and division situations. This presents new challenges.*

Children invent procedures for multiplying and dividing, just as they do for adding and subtracting. And, as was the case with addition and subtraction, these computational procedures are opportunities for children to encounter new ideas about units of ten, one hundred, one thousand, and so forth, and to build new understandings. But in the territory of multiplication and division, the issues encountered are different.

Multiplication and division are operations that differ in important ways from addition and subtraction. In both multiplication and division,

we are talking about taking a number of same-sized groups, where the
number in the group needn't be 1.[7] So, for instance, we can think about
24 groups of 6. If we think about what the 24 and the 6 might be in this
example, they describe different levels of organization: one number
describes a set (just as all numbers in addition and subtraction do), and
the other number describes a set of sets. Let's imagine that the 24 groups
of 6 are 24 baskets, each containing 6 pieces of fruit. The 6 is pieces of
fruit, but the 24 is baskets, which in this problem is the same as sets of 6.
This is very different from an addition or subtraction situation in which
we are talking about having, for example, 24 pieces of fruit and then
adding or subtracting 6 other pieces of fruit to or from them. These new
uses of number are difficult for children (Hiebert & Behr, 1988).

We can rewrite an addition problem that uses the numbers 24 and 6 to
highlight this comparison with multiplication: 24 + 6 can be thought of as
24 ones + 6 ones. In the multiplication problem using these numbers, our
24 baskets with 6 pieces of fruit each, we now ask for 24 sixes.

To compute the answer to the multiplication problem, we can collect
sets of 6 in different ways and still find the same answer: We can
compute 24 × 6 by first taking 20 × 6 and then 4 × 6 and adding the
resulting products, or by taking 4 × 6 and then adding that to 20 × 6,
or by taking 12 × 6 twice. Each of these computational approaches to
24 × 6 is an enactment of the distributive property of multiplication over
addition. Whether we think of 24 × 6 as (20 + 4)(6) = 20(6) + 4(6), or as
(12 + 12) (6 ) = 12(6) + 12(6), we are enacting a strategy that distributes the
multiplication over the addition to account for all of the groups identified
in the original problem. The property of chunking groups so that, when
combined, they form a certain number of sets of a certain size (in this
case, 24 sets of 6) is called *distributivity*.

While it is convenient to chunk numbers into tens because of our
base ten system, and conventional algorithms chunk the multiplication
and division processes by place or some power of ten, the value of using
tens, hundreds, thousands, and so on in the context of multiplication

---

[7] For our purposes here, we will work through this analysis with an "equal
groups" interpretation of multiplication and division. At the same time however,
we acknowledge that multiplication and division also apply to other situations,
including area, arrays, scaling, and combinations.

and division may not be obvious. Again, let's examine what might be involved in solving the problem 24 × 6, if our solution is to be tens-based. If we stick with our story of having 24 baskets, each with 6 pieces of fruit, one solution that makes use of groupings of ten is to take 2 groups of 10 baskets each, plus the remaining 4 baskets. If we were to write this with numbers, we might write (10 × 6) + (10 × 6) + (4 × 6). If we think about the 24 and 6 as multiunit numbers, keeping in mind the number of each sized unit that each represents, we might write this problem as:

$$[2(10) \times 6(1)] + [4(1) \times 6(1)]$$

This is not a simple idea to keep in mind, and the complexity only increases as the number of digits in the numbers being multiplied increases.

Some researchers (though relatively few, compared with those who study addition and subtraction) have aimed at characterizing and understanding how children make use of and build on their knowledge of the tens structure as they solve multidigit multiplication and division problems (Verschaffel et al., 2007). Rebecca Ambrose, Jae-Meen Baek, and Thomas Carpenter's (2003) study of children's invented procedures for multidigit multiplication and division provides one such analysis.[8]

Ambrose and colleagues studied six classrooms at third through fifth grade, observing in each class several times per week across one school year, and individually interviewing the children in three of the classes. The researchers, noting that the instructional context likely plays an important role in determining which strategies children do and do not use and how frequently they do so, describe several aspects of the classrooms they studied. These were classrooms in which teachers expected students to explain their own solutions to problems and to consider and analyze their classmates' solutions and reasoning. In fact, it was typical in these classrooms for four or five solutions to any given problem to be presented and discussed. Further, in each of these classrooms, teachers introduced both multiplication and division at the

---

[8] Similar analyses of multidigit division strategies are offered by Anghileri (2001), Baek (1998), Treffers (1987), and Van Putten, van den Brom-Snijders, and Beishuizen (2005).

same time; that is, none chose to work first on multiplication and later on division.

Ambrose and colleagues were specifically studying children's solutions to multiplication and division problems involving equal-sized groups of discrete objects, rather than area, rate, or other more abstract mulitiplicative situations. For these equal-groups problems, children's strategies for multidigit multiplication were of three general kinds. The most elementary of these were *modeling strategies*. The simplest modeling strategies involved no partitioning of either number. A child using this kind of strategy uses counters to individually represent each item in each group and counts these up, one at a time, to arrive at an answer. More complex modeling strategies involve the use of base ten materials such as blocks or drawings to model the problem. The researchers note that children using this type of strategy partition the number of items in each group (the multiplicand) while leaving the number of groups unpartitioned. For example, to model 24 cookies on each of 11 plates, children might create 11 piles of 2 tens blocks and 4 ones blocks each, then count the resulting total by tens and ones. With both modeling strategies—with and without a tens-based partitioning—children's solutions remained relatively tied to the specifics of the problem. They would not, for example, build the mathematically equivalent (but physically different) situation of 24 groups of 11.

Beyond the modeling strategies, Ambrose and colleagues found that children invented a variety of multidigit multiplication procedures that were *progressively more efficient strategies for adding*. These begin with simple repeated addition (adding 11 twenty-fours in our cookies example), and progress to doubling and other means of creating new units for accomplishing the multiplication. For the 11 plates of 24 cookies each, a child using doubling would add 24 + 24 to arrive at 48, and would then add 48 + 48 + 48 + 48 + 48. These five 48s account for 10 of the 11 plates; for the eleventh plate, the child adds one more 24. While doubling is common, it is not the only efficiency that children adopt. For example, they might calculate how many are in five groups and repeatedly use *that* new unit to efficiently add up the items in all the groups. While these strategies are not themselves concerned with tens structure, Ambrose and colleagues argue that such strategies offer children the opportunity to develop a concept that is critical to a tens-based strategy: that the multiplier can be partitioned. In the simpler modeling strategies, children don't partition the number representing the number of groups (the multiplier); however, with doubling and the other efficient adding procedures, the multiplier must be partitioned. That is, in our cookies problem, a child must have partitioned the multiplier (11) in order to know how many doublings of 24 are needed to calculate the total number of cookies on 11 plates, and in order to know that another 24 must be added to the sum of these doublings. In this case, the 11 groups are seen as 5 doublings plus 1, or 5(2) + 1.

The third general kind of strategy that children invented for multidigit multiplication was *procedures using tens*. Ambrose and colleagues describe two subtypes: those strategies in which a child partitions only one term into tens and ones, and those in which the child partitions both the multiplier and the multiplicand by tens and ones (this latter strategy being a relatively unusual invention). In Susannah's case 16, we see an example of a student partitioning a single term into tens and ones. The students are working on a problem that asks for the total number of starting players in the NCAA basketball tournament: 64 teams with 5 players starting on each team. Laurel solves it this way: "That would be 64 × 5. I use one 10 because I know 5 × 10 = 50. Then you do that six times. That's 30. I mean 300. Then you add 4 five times, which is 25, no 20. I added it all together and got 320." Ambrose and colleagues saw many similar examples. In addition, they offer the following example of the less commonly invented tens-partitioning of both factors.[9] In solving a problem about 43 boxes of cards with 24 cards in each box, one boy writes:

$$\begin{array}{c c}
\underline{\quad 4 \quad} & \underline{\quad 3 \quad} \\
800 & 60 \quad = \quad 860 \\
\\
160 & 12 \quad = \quad \underline{172} \\
& \qquad\quad 1032
\end{array}$$

What this child *hasn't* written is the 2 tens and 4 ones split that is implied by his calculations, with 2 (tens) to the left of the top row and 4 (ones) to the left of the bottom row. He has created a grid in which all the parts are multiplied: 20 × 40, 20 × 3, 4 × 40, and 4 × 3. It is exactly this logic that we see in Jayson's case 18 as Jackson, a ninth-grade student,

---

[9] Note that the multiplication algorithm historically taught in the U.S. relies on a tens-partitioning of both factors.

uses an area model to solve the problem 84 × 23, with an (80 + 4) by (20 + 3) rectangle. Building on this same logic, students in that ninth-grade class work out solutions for the multiplication of algebraic expressions such as $(x + 2)(x + 3)$.

Some students, who eventually succeed at decomposing both factors, begin their work on this strategy by correctly partitioning both factors, but losing track of all of the parts that need to be multiplied. We see an example of this in Susannah's case 16 as Josh works on the problem 18 × 12 and reasons, "I know 10 × 10 is 100 and 8 × 2 is 16, so if you add them together it would be 100 + 16 = 116." As his classmate David points out, "Josh didn't do 8 × 10," nor has he included the partial product 10 × 2. This is a work in progress for Josh, a kind of work that many children take on as they generalize what they know about addition to multiplication, and as they encounter the need to build, beyond that, strategies that are in accord with the distributive property.

Ambrose, Baek, and Carpenter's (2003) study focused not only on multiplication, but also on division. In general, they found that multiplication and division were of about equal difficulty for the children they observed and interviewed, with children adapting their multiplication strategies for use in solving division problems.[10] The researchers describe three general kinds of invented strategy for division of multidigit numbers: *working with one group at a time, working with multiple groups at a time*, and *decomposing the dividend*.

In most elementary multidigit division strategies, children work with one group at a time. Using repeated subtraction or addition, they may subtract one group at a time from the dividend until 0 is reached, or add one group at a time (from 0) until the dividend is reached, in either case counting the number of subtractions or additions to determine their answer. These same strategies can also be used in division situations that involve remainders. For these problems, the repeated subtraction or addition of groups ends when a number less than the divisor is left (i.e.,

---

[10] Note that this adaptation of multiplication computational procedures for division does not parallel the structures of the historically taught procedures. In the conventional algorithms, the multiplication procedure partitions both factors into units of different sizes (ones, tens, hundreds, etc.), but the division procedure essentially leaves the dividend whole (bringing down new parts as multiples of the divisor are subtracted).

Building a System of Tens

no more full groups can be subtracted or added). These repeated addition or subtraction strategies are more common for division problems in which the number of groups is the unknown: *If we have 72 flowers in bouquets of 12 flowers each, how many bouquets are there?* This can be solved simply by repeatedly subtracting 12 from 72 until 0 is reached, then counting the 6 twelves that were subtracted. But repeated subtraction or addition also works for partitive division problems, those in which we know the total and the number of groups, but not the number in each group: *If we have 72 flowers in 6 bouquets, how many flowers are in each bouquet?* Children visually represent each of the 6 groups (bouquets) and deal flowers out to each group, some number at a time, until all of the flowers are dealt out. They might deal out the flowers one by one until all flowers are in bouquets, finding that there are now 12 flowers in each bouquet. Or, they might deal the flowers out in larger numbers, let's say by twos, threes, or tens. (Even in these division strategies that deal with only one group at a time, it is worth noting that occasionally solutions accomplish a tens partitioning, whether in the partitive situations of dealing out 10 at a time to a certain number of groups, or in the grouping situations if the problem calls for 10 groups or the solution arrives at groups of 10.)

By contrast, strategies in which children work with multiple groups at a time are very commonly based on tens. One example that Ambrose and colleagues describe involves this problem: *How many candies would each of 17 friends have if 544 candies were equally shared among them?* Lynna begins by subtracting 170 from 544, labeling this "10 candies for each friend." Finding that there are still 374 candies remaining, she again subtracts 17 groups of 10 or 170, and then again, so that she has subtracted 30 groups of 17 from 544 with 34 candies remaining. Lynna finally subtracts 34, or "2 candies for each friend." The advance of Lynna's tens-based strategy over the strategies used for the flowers problem is that Lynna was able to think of the 17 tens as a unit to be subtracted; she does not need to deal out tens one at a time to build each separate group (whether bouquets or allotment of candies).

Finally, Ambrose and colleagues found that some children invent multidigit division procedures that decompose the dividend. This strategy turns out to be very inefficient.[11] Using this strategy, a child

---

[11] Nor is this the strategy used in the U.S. standard division algorithm, although in the U.S. standard algorithms for the other operations, we do decompose all numbers by place in this way.

breaks apart the dividend into ones, tens, hundreds, and so on, then calculates a quotient and a remainder for each part. Thus, for a problem that calls for 896 divided into groups of 35, a child would first divide the 6 ones, then the 90, and then the 800 by 35, keeping track of both the number of groups of 35 and the remainders for each subproblem, and then aggregating all of the results.

Among researchers there is wide agreement that for all four operations, including multiplication and division, teaching standard algorithms should not happen too early, and that computational procedures, invented or conventional, should grow from children's existing knowledge (Anghileri, Beishuizen, & van Putten, 2002; Treffers, 1987; Van Putten, van den Brom-Snijders, & Beishuizen, 2005; Verschaffel et al., 2007).

Even so, at this time, there is disagreement among researchers and among curriculum developers about the role of the historically taught algorithms in the mathematics curriculum. It is however clear that when such computational procedures are introduced to children who are still operating primarily with ones or with concrete physical representations, the mapping between the traditional algorithm and the problem is complicated and error-prone (e.g., Anghileri et al., 2002; Kamii, 1993; Lampert, 1986, 1992; Van Putten et al., 2005). Children might learn to perform the steps of these procedures without understanding what each step in the procedure accomplishes or how it relates to their own understanding, either of the problem or of the tens structure of number.

Let's return to those children in Ambrose, Baek, and Carpenter's (2003) study who solve multiplication problems by doubling, or Eleanor's students (case 15) who calculate $4 \times 27$ by doubling 27 and doubling again. What work might these students need to do in order to make sense of the conventional algorithm, which asks them first to compute $4 \times 7$, write the 8 below the line, then put a 2 over the 2 of 27, then multiply $4 \times 2$, add the carried 2 to that product, and write 10 in front of the 8, yielding an answer of 108? Clearly there is a great deal for a person to understand about how the groups are accounted for in this algorithm.

When we introduce conventional algorithms before giving children the opportunity to develop their own computational procedures, children do not at first see how, or if, the algorithm accounts for all the parts. For division, it is not clear to children why the long division procedure has them asking, for instance, how many 7s are in 10, when the real question is how many 7s are in 109.[12]  How conventional algorithms use groupings based on tens is not obvious to children who have not first worked from the kinds of invented procedures that Ambrose and colleagues describe. When instruction allows children to work first from their invented procedures, these groupings based on tens emerge from chidren's own solutions in meaningful ways (Anghileri et al., 2002; Van Putten et al., 2005; Lampert, 1986, 1992).

1005

SECTION 5

# Understanding decimal fractions

*Decimal fractions share some properties with whole numbers and some with common fractions. Many of the understandings of the system of tens that children build in the domain of whole number serve as important beginnings in their work to make sense of decimals and the kinds of fractional quantities they represent. Many new understandings must also be built.*

Decimal numbers are written with symbols that look like those we use for whole numbers, yet they represent fractional quantities. Decimal fractions indicate values between 0 and 1. So, for instance, no matter how large a (finite)[13] decimal fraction we add to the whole number 48, we know that the sum will approach, but never reach, the next whole number 49. The number 48.999999 is still less than one whole unit more than 48.

1010

1015

   As with common fractions, between any two decimal fractions there are an infinite number of decimals. Between 1.1 and 1.2, for instance,

---

[12] While this example assumes that the divisor (7) is the number in each group, the question, of course, can also be framed by using the divisor (7) as the number of groups: How many in a group if 109 is divided equally into 7 groups?

[13] The decimal 0.99999…, in which 9 repeats infinitely, is equal to 1.

there are the numbers 1.11 and 1.111 and 1.1111 and so on, as well as 1.12, 1.13, 1.14, ... . We can always add another place to the right that will add smaller and smaller amounts to the original number.

The kinds of fractions represented by decimals are created by successively partitioning the value of one place by ten. Tenths are created by partitioning the unit's value by ten; hundredths are created by partitioning tenths by ten; and so on. This is an important similarity between whole numbers and decimal fractions. And, as with whole numbers, the value of a decimal fraction is composed by both multiplication and addition. The number 0.234, for example, represents the quantity $[2(0.1) + 3(0.01) + 4(0.001)]$.

The story told by researchers about the development of children's understanding of decimal fractions can be thought of in two parts. In the 1980s and the early 1990s, researchers documented the many weaknesses and gaps in children's knowledge of decimals. It is important to underscore here that the lack of understanding documented in this era of research reflects some combination of the complexity of the mathematical ideas and the effectiveness of the most common decimal instruction at the time. This instruction often treated decimal numbers separately from fractions, ratios, and percents (with which they have much in common), offered procedures or rules for operating with decimal numbers, and provided few opportunities to represent these numbers with anything more concrete than number (base ten blocks, number lines, etc.) (Lachance & Confrey, 2002; Moss & Case, 1999).

The lack of understanding demonstrated by children in the studies conducted in the 1980s and early 1990s led researchers and curriculum writers to consider what kinds of instruction might help children to build stronger understandings of decimals. So while the earlier research commonly pointed to the errors that children made in understanding decimal numbers, more recent research points to some instructional approaches that may lead to stronger understandings of the quantities represented by decimal number and support the construction of sound procedures for operating on decimals. Both research literatures are informative, and we'll look at both.

From the earlier research, there is a relatively large body of literature on what children, given traditional instructional methods, don't know how to do with decimals. We learn from these studies that even middle school and high school students have significant difficulty ordering

Building a System of Tens

decimals, relating decimals to drawn representations, relating decimals to common fractions, and explaining the rationale for lining up the decimal points for the traditionally taught addition and subtraction algorithm. (Hiebert, 1992, Lachance and Confrey, 2002, and Moss and Case, 1999, review this literature.)

Many researchers believe that these difficulties are not surprising, given the nature of the quantities these numbers represent. Several lines of evidence suggest that human beings very naturally, and from a very early age, whether schooled or not (e.g., Carraher, Schliemann, & Carraher, 1988), think of numbers as what we get when we count things. Fractions, however, are not what we get from a simple counting. They result from dividing one quantity by another, and they are an expression of the relationship between these numbers. Thus, 0.7 represents the relationship 7 ÷ 10, or 7 of 10 parts, which is equivalent to the relationship expressed by 0.70 (70 ÷ 100), by 0.700 (700 ÷ 1,000), and so on. In whole number, of course, 7 and 70 and 700 represent different quantities.

The early research clearly showed that many of the errors children make when working with decimals are consistent with applying whole-number rules and procedures to decimal numbers. Two examples from research follow. A ninth grader writes 5.1 directly underneath 0.36 and says, "If you're adding 0.36 and 5.1 it would make a lot more sense if it came out to 0.8 or so" (Hiebert & Wearne, 1986). In 1981, more than half of all 13-year-olds in the United States were unable to correctly choose the largest among 0.19, 0.036, 0.195, and 0.2 (Carpenter, Corbitt, Kepner, Lindquist, & Reys, 1981). Many of these children selected 0.195 as the largest number, as it would be if all of the decimal points were removed.

Similar findings are reported by Lauren Resnick and her colleagues (1989). They conducted a study of 113 American, French, and Israeli fourth, fifth, and sixth graders, children who were in the early phases of their school work on decimals. These researchers were interested in whether or not children's interpretations of decimals could be described as being consistent with underlying rules. The rules of most interest to them were *the whole-number rule* and the *fraction rule*. According to the whole-number rule, children judge one decimal to be larger than another when it has more decimal places, as would be true of whole-number comparisons. Thus, children whose judgments are consistent with the whole-number rule would correctly say that 0.64 is larger than 0.2, but would incorrectly say that 0.64 is larger than 0.8. Resnick and her colleagues also reasoned that some children base their decimal comparisons on their knowledge

of common fractions, particularly their knowledge that the more parts
a whole is divided into, the smaller the parts. Children building on this
knowledge might interpret decimals according to a fraction rule,
judging that more decimal places indicate parts of smaller size, but
not simultaneously taking into account either how many of those
smaller-sized pieces are being denoted or the ratio expressed by each
decimal. These children, based on their knowledge that hundredths are
smaller than tenths, would correctly judge 0.64 to be smaller than 0.8, but
would incorrectly judge 0.64 also to be smaller than 0.2.

By asking children to make a variety of judgments of this kind and
through other interview questions about decimals, Resnick and her
coworkers found that, to a very high degree, children's responses either
were consistent with one of these two rules (or with a less common
variant of the whole-number rule, in which children treated decimals with
a zero in the tenths place as a special case), or were correct for all items.

This research makes very clear that (1) in the United States, following
the whole-number rule is the most commonly occurring error pattern
among children who are just beginning to work with decimals, and (2)
children are making sense of the decimal-fraction system by trying to
connect it with the kind of number system for which they already have
some working knowledge. This productive strategy also leads to errors;
but these errors are an important source of information to a teacher, and a
source of discussion and new opportunities for learning for the class.

In Nicole's case 25, we see students making judgments similar to those
that a whole-number rule would generate. A group of students working
on a word problem about a jeweler and grams of gold add 1.14, 0.089,
and 0.3 by aligning them on the right as they would for whole numbers,
arriving at an answer of 2.06. A little later in the class discussion, one of
the students in this group asserts that a classmate's answer of 1.529 is too
big. He believes that 1.529 is larger than his own answer of 2.06. For him,
it is as if the decimal points are not there and these numbers are to be
treated as whole numbers.

Kathryn Irwin's (1996) research with 11- and 12-year-old students
provides some detailed illustration of the complexity of students' work
in sorting out which aspects of their whole-number knowledge apply to
decimal fractions and which must be adapted. Irwin reports on one pair
of students who are considering the question, Is one hundredth written
as 0.100 or as 0.01? The students thought that 0.100 looked right, but

they also knew that the number 0.355 was called 355 thousandths, and it didn't make sense to them that 0.100 would be hundredths if 0.355 was thousandths. These students also wondered if there were a "oneths" column. If 0.100 were to be the way to write one hundredth, then, they reasoned, there needed to be a oneths column, along with the tenths and hundredths columns. We see in this example students trying to align what they know about spoken number and written number across all of the place value system, both whole numbers and decimal fractions. Their questions about how to write the numbers belie their questions about the meanings and values of the places to the right of the decimal point and how these values are related to whole-number values.

All of this research uncovering children's struggles with the meaning of decimal fractions leads to the question of what kind of learning opportunities can help students to build stronger conceptions of these numbers. The work of James Hiebert, Diana Wearne, and Susan Taber (1991) begins to show some of what it takes for students to go beyond these initial conceptions. Hiebert and his colleagues studied one classroom of fourth-grade children, for whom they provided 11 days of decimal fraction study. Their instruction was aimed at using concrete, physical representations to help children develop clearer meanings for tenths, hundredths, and so on. As a result of their intervention, Hiebert et al. found that children became more and more likely to offer correct, quantitative interpretations of decimals, to represent decimal fractions with concrete materials, and to make correct comparisons among different decimal numbers.

Returning to Nicole's case 25, in which students are working to add the numbers 1.14, 0.089, and 0.3, we see students doing work very similar to that reported by Hiebert et al. (1991). They call upon their understandings of the numbers—and the different places—to decide how to add, explaining the reason they didn't line up all the numbers was that "we needed to line up the tenths with the tenths and the hundredths with the hundredths to make it come out right." In order to convince their classmates, and themselves, students represented the decimal quantities with blocks. The students, including those who had initially solved the problem incorrectly, were intrigued; they continued to make up new problems to solve as they worked further to understand the mathematics of these numbers.

Hiebert et al.'s 1991 study began to get at what would happen if students could create and work with some physical representation of the quantities expressed by decimal fractions. And as we see both in Hiebert et al.'s results and in Nicole's case, there is some benefit gained. This is one of the studies that begins the second part of the research story on the development of children's understanding of decimal fractions. This second part of the story focuses on the study of how children come to build strong conceptions of decimal fractions. The methods used by the researchers doing this work are design experiment methods; that is, they try out new instructional approaches to decimals in classrooms, carefully studying the students' knowledge before, during, and after the instruction. In this set of studies, one instructional shift that stands out is an emphasis on teaching and learning about decimal number in the context of a broader study of ratio (Moss & Case, 1999, 2002; Lachance & Confrey, 1995, 2002).

Two groups of researchers, Joan Moss and Robbie Case in Canada and Andrea Lachance and Jere Confrey in the United States, conducted similar studies with similar findings. Each group designed an instructional approach to ratio, fraction, decimal, and percent. Moss and Case's study involved lessons for fourth-grade students, while the Lachance and Confrey (1995, 2002) study involved a sequence of lessons presented across three years to one cohort of students as they went from third grade through fifth grade. Moss and Case (1999) describe the similarities between the approaches of these two groups. They write that in each program:

> a strong emphasis was placed (a) on continuous quantity and measurement, as opposed to discrete quantity and counting; (b) on splitting as a natural form of computation that can be used in a measurement context; and (c) on the equivalence among different forms of rational number representation. (p. 143)

There were also a number of differences between the programs on potentially important details, including the representations they introduced to children and the order in which they treated topics. Still, in both contexts, students demonstrated impressive success in reasoning correctly about decimal quantities and showed evidence of basing their reasoning on arguments of proportionality, in striking comparison with the results of earlier research, or (in the case of the Moss and Case study) in striking comparison with similar students who had more traditional instruction in decimal number. Some examples from their studies give a sense of their findings and the kind of understandings that children in their programs demonstrated. However, both the Moss and Case study and the Lachance and Confrey study used many different test items to get a clear picture of the children's understanding, and the examples below are selected from among the many results they describe.

Lachance and Confrey (2002) found that students participating in their program were quite adept at, among other things, ordering decimal numbers. In fact, 14 of the 20 fifth-grade students completed all ten of the decimal ordering questions correctly. So, for example, when asked which was larger, 0.8 or 0.34, most students responded correctly. Illustrating the reasoning that they heard on interviewing students, Lachance and Confrey quote one student: "'0.8 is eight-tenths and 0.34 is thirty-four hundredths. I know that 8 is closer to 10 than 34 is to 100, so 0.8 must be bigger.'" They go on to write: "When questioned further about his reasoning, the student indicated that he was thinking it took 10 tenths to make a whole and 100 hundredths to make a whole. Thus, his reasoning was that 0.34 was further from one whole than 0.8 was" (p. 518).

Similarly, Moss and Case (1999) found that the students who participated in their experimental program could all correctly answer the questions, "Is there a number between 0.3 and 0.4? Can you name one?" While these students and the comparison group receiving more traditional decimal instruction performed similarly on this item before instruction, only 15 percent of the students receiving the more traditional instruction in decimals correctly answered this question on the post-test. They offer these sample quotes:

| | |
|---|---|
| Experimenter: | Can you think of a number that lies between decimal 3 and decimal 4?[14] |
| Experimental S1: | Well, point three five is between point three and point four. |
| Experimental S2: | Decimal three zero nine. |
| Control S1: | There is no number between decimal three and decimal four. |
| Control S2: | Point zero three. (p. 135) |

---

[14] This construction, "decimal 3," corresponds to "point 3," the common U.S. term for this same quantity.

A second example from Moss and Case's fourth-grade students suggests that they were using this kind of proportional reasoning even when the problem was beyond their immediate grasp. In one of the interview questions, students were asked, "Could these be the same amount: decimal zero six of a tenth and decimal six of a hundredth?" This question asks the students to think about operating on decimal quantities; it asks, What is the relationship between the quantities $(0.06 \times 0.1)$ and $(0.6 \times 0.01)$? They quote two students from the experimental program and one from the control group:

Experimental S1:     No, they have to be different. Hey wait; no, maybe they are the same. Yes, because decimal zero six to one tenth is kinda like 6 to 100.

Experimental S2:     I don't know because decimal six is bigger than decimal zero six but also one tenth is bigger than one hundredth.

By contrast, the students in the control group tended to use additive instead of ratio-based strategies, as exemplified by this response:

Control S1:     No, they can't be the same because if you take 6 away [from 10], there would only be 4 left; if you take 6 away [from 100] there would be 94 left. (p. 137)

The research evidence from Moss and Case (1999, 2002) and from Lachance and Confrey (1995, 2002) suggests that children may develop stronger understandings of decimal numbers and operating with decimal numbers when the instruction focuses on ratio. This shift in the research community to an interest in embedding students' work with decimal number in a broader study of ratio is accompanied by a related shift in published curriculum materials. Beginning in the late 1990s, new mathematics curricula were published that treat decimal numbers as they relate to fractions and percent, in which ratio is at least implicitly, if not also explicitly treated (e.g., TERC's *Investigations in Number, Data, and Space* (2008), *What's That Portion?* and *Decimals on Grids and Number Lines*, and Lappan et al.'s *Connected Mathematics Program* (2006), *Bits and Pieces I, II, and III*). While there are not yet studies of the decimal understandings students build by using these new curricula, the results from Moss and Case and Lachance and Confrey are encouraging about this general approach.

Building a System of Tens

In the second Moss and Case example excerpted here, we have a glimpse of a few children's reasoning about the multiplication of decimal numbers. In the cases of chapter 7, we have some more detailed looks at children who are working to understand the issues that arise while multiplying and dividing decimal numbers. But there is remarkably little research on this topic.

The multiplication and division of decimal numbers arises in a study conducted by Anna Graeber and Dina Tirosh (1990), with a slightly different focus. These researchers find that fourth- and fifth-grade children are more likely to correctly solve word problems involving the multiplication or division of one whole number and one decimal number if the decimal number refers to the amount in a group (e.g., jelly beans cost $0.80 for 1 pound, how much for 5 pounds?) than if the decimal number refers to the number of groups (e.g., cheese costs $6 for 1 pound, how much for 0.8 pounds?). In this latter case, students tended to write incorrect division equations. This result, though certainly one of interest, is not focused on students' understanding of the tens structure of these numbers.

Cinzia Bonotto (2005) conducted a teaching experiment that is more directly concerned with our topic. Agreeing with a point of view expressed by other researchers (Hiebert, 1985; Irwin, 2001), that representations well connected to students' existing understandings are important to student learning about decimal number, Bonotto was interested in learning how students might use their knowledge from a well-known out-of-school context to support their thinking about the multiplication of decimal numbers. She designed a set of six lessons (of about 90 minutes each) using grocery shopping receipts. These lessons were taught in two fourth-grade classrooms in Italy. In early lessons, the receipts listed the item purchased, the weight of the item, the cost in lire per kilogram, and the price charged for the amount of the item purchased. In later lessons, the price paid was missing. For example, one such receipt included this item: SALMON – 0.106 kg; 74,500 lire/kg; _____ lire. Children were asked, *Will you spend more or less than 74,500 lire for the salmon? Explain your answer*. Bonotto found that children drew on everyday knowledge in their reasoning about these grocery problems. With a problem such as the one about the price of salmon, children tended to reason that because they were buying less than one kilogram, the cost would be less than 74,500 lire, or the price they would pay if buying a whole kilogram. Most students invented procedures for carrying out the necessary multiplications that involved partitioning the weight into convenient parts, then calculating the cost for each part and summing across these partial products.

This study offers evidence of children inventing sensible tens-based multiplication procedures for decimal numbers, but it is too limited in scope to offer the kind of taxonomy of multiplication strategies (or for that matter, division strategies) that we have for whole number. Nor does it begin to explore the complexities of unit that arise in the context of multiplying and dividing decimal fractions. Yet the issues encountered are complex. In the absence of other research on this topic, let's return to our cases.

In Leslie's case 28, we see a sixth-grade class working on the following problem: *Mr. Smith needs new carpet for one of his rooms. The room measures 11.1 meters by 15.3 meters. How much carpeting should Mr. Smith order?* It is early in the school year (October), and Leslie notes that as she begins to work with the class on the multiplication of decimals, most students are able to correctly use a computational algorithm they have learned in previous grades. But when she asks the students to represent the problem using a diagram or base ten materials, many students struggle. If we look at Chad's work next to Tori's work on this problem, we begin to see some of the mathematical work facing students as they encounter decimal numbers in the context of multiplication.

Chad has correctly computed that 11.1 × 15.3 = 169.83. His drawing shows a grid 15 units by 11 units, with three squares (roughly equal in size to the 15 ones) extending beyond the first row of the 15-by-11 array, and with a single small square (again roughly equal in size to the units) extending the first column of the 11. The dimensions are labeled 15.3 and 11.1, but while the 15 and the 11 are multiplied or crossed with one another in this area model, creating the grid, the decimal portions of each number remain unmultiplied. Chad knows that his drawing doesn't capture the situation. He sees that his 11-by-15 grid accounts for 165 of the 169.83 required, and he counts each tenth for 0.4 more. But Chad is troubled by the missing 4.43. Whether it is the need to create units of different sizes and represent them in the same multiplication image, coordinating the various units that this problem entails (hundreds, tens, ones, tenths, hundredths), or understanding that it is even possible to multiply quantities smaller than one, or some other issue, we don't know. But if we look at Tori's solution, we see in it some of the ideas that children must construct as they multiply decimal numbers.

1320

1325

1330

1335

1340

1345

1350

Building a System of Tens

Tori, like Chad, has correctly computed a solution to this problem using the conventional multiplication algorithm. Unlike Chad, Tori has also drawn an accurate representation of the multiplication implied by this problem. And because of that, she is able to learn quite a bit. Her drawing shows a 15.3-by-11.1 rectangle. The 15.3 is partitioned into 10 + 5 + 0.3. The dimension that is 11.1 in length is partitioned into 10 + 1 + 0.1. The regions of this rectangle with whole-number factors are labeled with their products 100 + 50 + 10 + 5. Along the bottom are the *tenths* created by multiplying the 1 tenth of 11.1 by the 10 and the 5, a total of 15 tenths, as well as the 3 hundredths created by multiplying (and in the case of the drawing, the crossing of the lines representing each kind of unit) the 1 tenth by the 3 tenths.[15] To the right are 3 columns of 11 tenths each, representing the multiplication of the 0.3 from 15.3 and the 11 from 11.1. Tori creates these units as part of her drawing, but as we learn from her conversation afterward, she wasn't anticipating them, nor, with the hundredths, was she at first even able to label the unit that she had drawn. Here, Tori is apparently working at putting together two different notions: first, that in multiplying a number less than 1 by another number, the product is smaller than that other number (and so if both numbers are smaller than 1, the product will be smaller than both numbers, as is the case with $0.1 \times 0.3$ in this problem); and second, that in multiplying decimal fractions, sometimes new units are created. But understanding how and when these units are created and what their quantitative relationships are to one another is not simple.

Finally, if we consider *dividing* decimal numbers, there are again many new ideas to encounter. In Bernard's case 29, we see an eighth-grade class as they work on the problem $49.92 \div 15.6$. Different students calculate the answer differently. By the end of the class one student, Sarah, notes: "Look at the problems on the board. We have $49.92 \div 15.6$, $499.2 \div 156$, and $4,992 \div 1,560$, and they all have the same answer." Bernard then says, "So, here is something I want you to think about. Why is it these problems have the same answer of 3.2? Why can we move the

---

[15] Looking at Tori's diagram, you may at first find her tenths somewhat confusing. They are not small enough to be drawn to scale. Tory's tenths along the bottom of the diagram are the length of a one in the rest of the diagram, and so would need to be only one tenth as deep to be accurate.

decimal and get the same result? Why does it work for division and not multiplication?" These are difficult and related questions.

Let's begin with Bernard's first question: Why do all of these different problems have the same answer, 3.2? In order to answer this question, we must ask what 3.2 means in each of these problems. In the case of 49.92 ÷ 15.6, it may mean that there are 3.2 groups of 15.6 in 49.92.[16] In the problem in which the decimal places of each number have been moved one place, multiplying each number by 10 (499.2 ÷ 156), we can think of the 3.2 as the number of groups of 156 in 499.2. And finally, the same ratio applies to the version of the problem in which the decimal places have been moved two places in each number, effectively multiplying the original quantities by 100. Dividing decimal numbers using the conventional long division algorithm, or any algorithm that involves the moving of decimal points in order to work with whole numbers, brings children face to face with not only the ratio implied by each decimal fraction itself, but now also the ratio expressed by the division problem and the equivalent expressions created by multiplying the dividend and the divisor by the same power of ten.

We have seen across the sections of this chapter how much work children must do in order to sort out the relationship between ones and tens in whole numbers and to stay mindful of this relationship while operating with multidigit numbers. The issue is no less complex in the case of decimal fractions; children must keep in mind that one tenth is both 1 tenth and 10 hundredths. Nor is it the case that these children, who years before sorted out at least some aspects of these tens relations for whole numbers, can in some quick and simple way transfer that understanding to the quantities represented by the infinite number of places we can create to the right of the decimal point. Further, students must come to see how through multiplication and division, new units are created (e.g., in multiplying 1 tenth by 1 tenth, the product is 1 hundredth) and new ratios encountered. What we know to be true is this:

[16] Alternatively, of course, it could mean that there are 15.6 in each of 3.2 groups; or, if this refers to an area situation, it could mean that for an area of 49.92, if 15.6 is one dimension, then 3.2 is the other, and so forth.

By building on their earlier understandings of whole number in the base ten system and by building a strong new sense of the ratios these decimal fractions express, children come to know what decimal fractions mean, gaining some sense of the power and elegance of the decimal system along with a facility for operating in it.

# Conclusion

The ideas that children confront as they try to make sense of place value are very complex. We know more about the development of children's understandings of some of these ideas than we do about others. Perhaps we know least about children's understandings of (1) very large numbers, (2) very small numbers (multidigit decimal fractions), and (3) the effects of multiplication and division on powers of ten, especially in the context of decimal numbers. With respect to any of the five themes examined here, however, we are all still learning about the ideas that children begin with, and how they come to build stronger conceptions. We move toward a clearer picture of this as teachers and researchers continue to make public their thoughtful and careful observations of children building a system of tens.

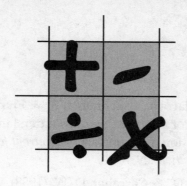

# References

Ambrose, R., Baek, J., & Carpenter, T. P. (2003). Children's inventions of multidigit multiplication and division algorithms. In A. J. Baroody & A. Dowker (Eds.), *The development of arithmetic concepts and skills* (pp. 305–336). Mahwah, NJ: Erlbaum.

Anghileri, J. (2001). Development of division strategies for year 5 pupils in ten English schools. *British Educational Research Journal, 27*(1), 85–103.

Anghileri, J., Beishuizen, M., & Van Putten, K. (2002). From informal strategies to structured procedures: Mind the gap. *Educational Studies in Mathematics, 49*, 149–170.

Baek, J. (1998). Children's invented algorithms for multidigit multiplication problems. In L. Morrow & M. Kenney (Eds.), *NCTM yearbook: The teaching and learning of algorithms in school mathematics* (pp. 151–160). Reston, VA: NCTM.

Beishuizen, M. (1993). Mental strategies and materials or models for addition and subtraction up to 100 in Dutch second grades. *Journal for Research in Mathematics Education, 24*, 294–323.

Bonotto, C. (2005). How informal out-of-school mathematics can help students make sense of formal in-school mathematics: The case of multiplying by decimal numbers. *Mathematical Thinking and Learning, 7*(4), 313–344.

Booth, J. L., & Siegler, R. S. (2006). Developmental and individual differences in pure numerical estimation. *Developmental Psychology, 41*, 189–201.

Carpenter, T. P., Corbitt, M. K., Kepner, H. S., Lindquist, M. M., & Reys, R. E. (1981). Decimals: Results and implications from the second NAEP mathematics assessment. *Arithmetic Teacher, 28*(8), 34–37.

Carpenter, T. P., Fennema, E., & Franke, M. I. (1996). Cognitively Guided Instruction: A knowledge base for reform in primary mathematics instruction. *Elementary School Journal 97*(1), 3–20.

Carpenter, T. P., Franke, M. L., Jacobs, V., Fennema, E., & Empson, S. B. (1998). A longitudinal study of intervention and understanding in children's multidigit addition and subtraction. *Journal for Research in Mathematics Education, 29*, 3–20.

Carraher, T. N., Schliemann, A. D., & Carraher, D. W. (1988). Mathematical concepts in everyday life. In G. B. Saxe & M. Gearhart (Eds.), *New Directions for Child Development*, No. 41. San Francisco: Jossey-Bass.

Cobb, P. (1995). Cultural tools and mathematical learning: A case study. *Journal for Research in Mathematics Education, 26*, 362–385.

Cobb, P., & Wheatley, G. (1988). Children's initial understandings of ten. *Focus on Learning Problems in Mathematics, 10*, 1–28.

Fuson, K. C. (1990). Conceptual structures for multiunit numbers: Implications for learning and teaching multidigit addition, subtraction, and place-value. *Cognition and Instruction, 7*, 343–404.

Fuson, K. C. (2003). Developing mathematical power in whole number operations. In J. Kilpatrick, W. G. Martin, & D. Schifter (Eds.), *A research companion to Principles and Standards for School Mathematics* (pp. 68–94). Reston, VA: NCTM.

Fuson, K. C., Smith, S. T., & LoCicero, A. M. (1997). Supporting Latino first graders' ten-structured thinking in urban classrooms. *Journal for Research in Mathematics Education, 28*, 738–760.

Fuson, K. C., Wearne, D., Hiebert, J. C., Murray, H. G., Human, P. G., Olivier, A. I., Carpenter, T. C., & Fennema, E. (1997). Children's conceptual structures for multidigit numbers and methods of multidigit addition and subtraction. *Journal for Research in Mathematics Education, 28*, 130–162.

Graeber, A. O., & Tirosh, D. (1990). Insights fourth and fifth graders bring to multiplication and division with decimals. *Educational Studies in Mathematics, 21*, 565–588.

Hiebert, J. (1985). Children's knowledge of common and decimal fractions. *Education and Urban Society, 17*, 427–437.

Hiebert, J. (1992). Mathematical, cognitive, and instructional analyses of decimal fractions. In G. Leinhardt, R. Putnam, & R. A. Hattrup (Eds.), *Analysis of arithmetic for mathematics teaching* (pp. 283–322). Hillsdale, NJ: Erlbaum.

Hiebert, J. & Behr, M. (1988). Introduction. In J. Hiebert & M. Behr (Eds.), *Number concepts and operations in the middle grades* (pp. 1–18). Hillsdale, NJ and Reston, VA: Erlbaum and NCTM.

Hiebert, J., & Wearne, D. (1986). Procedures over concepts: The acquisition of decimal number knowledge. In J. Hiebert (Ed.), *Conceptual and procedural knowledge: The case of mathematics* (pp. 199–223). Hillsdale, NJ: Erlbaum.

Hiebert, J., Wearne, D., & Taber, S. (1991). Fourth-graders' gradual construction of decimal fractions during instruction using different physical representations. *The Elementary School Journal, 91*(4), 321–341.

Irwin, K. (1996, April). *Why are decimal fractions difficult?* Paper presented at the annual meeting of the American Educational Research Association, New York.

Irwin, K. (2001). Using everyday knowledge of decimals to enhance understanding. *Journal for Research in Mathematics Education, 32,* 399–420.

Jacobs, V. R. (2002). A longitudinal study of invention and understanding: Children's multidigit addition and subtraction. In J. Sowder & B. Schappelle (Eds.), *Lessons learned from research* (pp. 93–100). Reston, VA: NCTM.

Kamii, C. (1989). *Young children continue to reinvent arithmetic – 2nd grade: Implications of Piaget's theory.* New York: Teachers College Press.

Kamii, C. (1993). *Young children continue to reinvent arithmetic – 3rd grade: Implications of Piaget's theory.* New York: Teachers College Press.

Kamii, C., Lewis, B. A., & Livingston, S. J. (1993). Primary arithmetic: Children inventing their own procedures. *Arithmetic Teacher, 41,* 200–203.

Kilpatrick, J., Swafford, J., & Findell, B. (2001). *Adding it up: Helping children learn mathematics.* Washington, D.C.: National Academy Press.

Lachance, A. & Confrey, J. (1995, October). *Introducing fifth graders to decimal notation through ratio and proportion.* Paper presented at the annual meeting of the North American Chapter of the International Group for the Psychology of Mathematics Education, Columbus, OH.

Lachance, A. & Confrey, J. (2002). Helping students build a path of understanding from ratio and proportion to decimal notation. *Journal of Mathematical Behavior, 20,* 503–526.

Lampert, M. (1986). Knowing, doing, and teaching multiplication. *Cognition and Instruction, 3,* 305–342.

Lampert, M. (1992). Teaching and learning long division for understanding in school. In G. Leinhardt, R. Putnam, & R. A. Hattrup (Eds.), *Analysis of arithmetic for mathematics teaching* (pp. 221–282). Hillsdale, NJ: Erlbaum.

Lappan, G., Fey, J. T., Fitzgerald, W. M., Friel, S. N., & Phillips, E. D. (2006). *Connected Mathematics 2. Bits and Pieces I, II, and III.* Boston, MA: Pearson.

Madell, R. (1985). Children's natural processes. *Arithmetic Teacher, 32*(7), 20–22.

McClain, K., Cobb, P., & Bowers, J. (1998). A contextual investigation of three-digit addition and subtraction. In L. J. Morrow & M. J. Kenney (Eds.), *NCTM yearbook: The teaching and learning of algorithms in school mathematics* (pp. 141–150). Reston, VA: NCTM.

Miura, I., & Okamoto, Y. (2003). Language supports for mathematics understanding and performance. In A. J. Baroody & A. Dowker (Eds.), *The development of arithmetic concepts and skills* (pp. 229–242). Mahwah, NJ: Erlbaum.

Moss, J., & Case, R. (1999). Developing children's understanding of the rational numbers: A new model and an experimental curriculum. *Journal for Research in Mathematics Education, 30,* 122–147.

Moss, J., & Case, R. (2002). Developing children's understanding of the rational numbers. In J. Sowder & B. Chapelle (Eds.), *Lessons learned from research* (pp. 143–150). Reston, VA: NCTM.

Opfer, J. E., & Siegler, R. S. (2007). Representational change and children's numerical estimation. *Cognitive Psychology, 55,* 169–195.

Resnick, L. B. (1992). From protoquantities to operators: Building mathematical competence on a foundation of everyday knowledge. In G. Leinhardt, R. Putnam, & R. A. Hattrup (Eds.), *Analysis of arithmetic for mathematics teaching* (pp. 373–429). Hillsdale, NJ: Erlbaum.

Resnick, L. B., Lesgold, S., & Bill, V. (1990, July). *From protoquantities to number sense*. Paper presented at the International Group for the Psychology of Mathematics Education, Mexico City.

Resnick, L. B., Nesher, P., Leonard, F., Magone, M., Omanson, S., & Peled, I. (1989). Conceptual bases of arithmetic errors: The case of decimal fractions. *Journal for Research in Mathematics Education*, 20(1), 8–27.

Ross, S. (1989). Parts, wholes, and place value: A developmental view. *Arithmetic Teacher*, 36(6), 47–51.

Seron, X., Deloche, G., & Noel, M. P. (1992). Number transcribing by children: Writing Arabic numbers under dictation. In J. Bideaud, C. Meljac, & J-P. Fischer (Eds.), *Pathways to number* (pp. 245–264). Hillsdale, NJ: Erlbaum.

Seron, X., & Fayol, M. (1994). Number transcoding in children: A functional analysis. *British Journal of Developmental Psychology*, 12, 281–300.

Siegler, R. S., & Booth, J. L. (2004). Development of numerical estimation in young children. *Child Development*, 75, 428–444.

Siegler, R. S., & Booth, J. L. (2005). Development of numerical estimation: A review. In J. I. D. Campbell (Ed.), *Handbook of mathematical cognition* (pp. 197–212). New York: Psychology Press.

Siegler, R. S., & Opfer, J. (2003). The development of numerical estimation: Evidence for multiple representations of numerical quantity. *Psychological Science*, 14, 237–243.

Skwarchuk, S-L., & Anglin, J. (2002). Children's acquisition of the English cardinal number words: A special case of vocabulary development. *Journal of Educational Psychology*, 94(1), 107–125.

Steffe, L. (1988). Children's construction of number sequences and multiplying schemes. In J. Hiebert & M. Behr (Eds.), *Number concepts and operations in the middle grades* (pp. 119–140). Hillsdale, NJ, and Reston, VA: Erlbaum and NCTM.

Steffe, L. P., Cobb, P., & Von Glasersfeld, E. (1988). *Construction of arithmetical meanings and strategies*. New York: Springer-Verlag.

TERC. (2008). *Investigations in number, data, and space* (2nd ed.). *What's That Portion?* and *Decimals on Grids and Number Lines*. Glenview, IL: Pearson Education.

Towse, J., & Saxton, M. (1998). Mathematics across national boundaries: Cultural and linguistic perspectives on numerical competence. In C. Donlan (Ed.), *The development of mathematical skills* (pp. 129–150). Hove, England: Psychology Press.

Treffers, A. (1987). *Three dimensions: A model of goal and theory description in mathematics education – The Wiskobas project*. Dordrecht, The Netherlands: Reidel.

Van Putten, C. M., van den Brom-Snijders, P., & Beishuizen, M. (2005). Progressive mathematization of long division in Dutch primary schools. *Journal for Research in Mathematics Education, 36*, 44–73.

Varelas, M., & Becker, J. (1997). Children's developing understanding of place value: Semiotic aspects. *Cognition and Instruction, 15*(2), 265–286.

Verschaffel, L., Greer, B., & De Corte, E. (2007). Whole number concepts and operations. In F. K. Lester (Ed.), *Second handbook of research on mathematics teaching and learning* (pp. 557–628). Charlotte, NC: Information Age Publishing.

Wood, T. (1996). Events in learning mathematics: Insights from research in classrooms. *Educational Studies in Mathematics, 30*, 85–105.

Building a System of Tens